PAWS FOR THOUGHT

PAWS FOR THOUGHT

HEATHER COOK

PHOTOGRAPHS BY ROGER COOK

Matador
9 Priory Business Park,
Wistow Road, Kibworth Beauchamp,
Leicestershire. LE8 0RX
Tel: (+44) 116 279 2299
Fax: (+44) 116 279 2277
Email: books@troubador.co.uk
Web: www.troubador.co.uk/matador

ISBN 978 1783061 457

British Library Cataloguing in Publication Data.
A catalogue record for this book is available from the British Library.

Typeset in 12pt Book Antiqua by Troubador Publishing Ltd, Leicester, UK

Matador is an imprint of Troubador Publishing Ltd

Printed and bound in the UK by TJ International, Padstow, Cornwall

MIX
Paper from
responsible sources
FSC® C013056

This book is dedicated to my mother, Jean, who passed away in 2012.

INTRODUCTION

A Very Special Cat

Years of rescuing and re-homing cats and kittens failed utterly to dull the fascination of their fuzzy charms and complex personalities. In fact, the more I had to do with the feline race the more I admired their infinite variety and wide-ranging talents. When at last I stepped down as homing officer for Woking Branch of Cats Protection, I still had what many sensible people would consider to be a ridiculous number of cats, most of whom had special needs of one sort or another. On one occasion when I rushed into the local supermarket for an emergency top-up of cat food, the lady on the check-out viewed the cascading heap of tins and pouches with amazement and asked me how many cats I had.

'We're down to nineteen now,' I said with a wistful smile. 'We lost three of our pensioners recently.'

Her smile was an uneasy combination of pity and panic as she attempted to avoid being crushed by a landslide of feline goodies.

It's a couple of years now since the cat pens were reallocated to the younger and more robust members of the local branch, but Poor Roger and I still have our own feline Special Needs Unit, comprising a number of "Golden Oldies", as well as our beloved brain-damaged Benjamin Wobble and St Petersburg Cloud Princess – a

Persian with every allergy known to cats and probably to giraffes in Kenya. We also have several cats with what could loosely be termed "challenging personalities", including Evie, the author of my previous book.

And then there is Stumpy Malone, who came to us as a kitten just as we had resolved – very firmly – not to take on any more youngsters. Stumpy was born without back paws, but this certainly doesn't matter to Stumpy, who is game for anything. There is something inspiring about this little black cat who is so happy to be alive and so excited by the world around him; for animals have a wisdom that humans have long forgotten. They know that age is just a number and disability is just a word: the important thing is to concentrate on what you can do rather than what you can't – a lesson that Stumpy mastered at an early age.

This is Stumpy's story and I hope you will enjoy reading about our brave little boy and the rest of our feline family. Luckily he has two very well-developed front paws and his keyboard skills are legendary in these parts.

CHAPTER ONE

My Early Days

I'm sick of being told that kittenhood is the happiest time of your life. Believe me, hiding away down the side of that dilapidated old shed didn't do much for me, particularly as our poor old mother had hardly any milk and my brother Woody kept standing on me to secure the best suckling position. Mum was small and black, like me, and Woody was striped – like a very thin humbug.

When it rained the water would cascade off the shed roof and we'd huddle under Mum's tummy to keep dry. We had another little brother who didn't make it, but life was tough and we soon stopped thinking about him as we needed all our strength to survive. More than anything, I remember the awful gnawing hunger pains which never went away.

The smell in our den was terrible and Mum said this was a mixture of tomcat and foxes. She hated the foxes and when old Freddie Fox came huffing and puffing round late at night she'd growl and spit at him. Once, he shoved his great pointed muzzle close to where we were lying and she raked her claws across his snout. Shining beads of blood oozed through his fur and he beat a hasty retreat. Serve him right!

She wasn't all that keen on the old tabby tomcat either. Seemed to blame him for everything and said she would have been much better off if she'd never given in to his manly desires, whatever that might mean. Anyway, every time he showed up she screamed and stamped her foot, so he'd look at her as if she'd gone mad, spray all over the shed and then leave.

Things were even worse when we began to fancy something a bit more substantial than watery milk because Mum would disappear for hours on end, then come back with something really yummy like a soggy crust or a lump of rancid bacon fat. Just as things were looking about as cheerful as a baboon with a boil on its bum, we heard a great commotion and a human was peering down at us. It was a female human and in her hand she held a plate of delicious-smelling food. Our mother was growling and trying to position herself between us and the plate, but Woody and I couldn't resist the smell and disobeyed her for the first time in our lives.

This went on for several days and we soon got to know the voice that went with the food. We didn't let the woman touch us, but we tucked in while she waited and talked to us in a quiet, pleasant voice. Even Mum began to relax enough to mop up the remains of the feast once the woman had gone and it came as a shock when our friend turned up one day with two other women. One of them was carrying a huge metal cage thing, which I later learned was a trap, and the other one had a smaller box with bars on the front. Our friend put the food down as usual and kept mumbling about how guilty she felt about betraying out trust, but Woody and I were so hungry that we hurled ourselves into the plate. Before we knew what was happening, one of these other women had grabbed both of us by the scruff of the neck and hoisted us into the air.

'One tabby, one black – both boys. And this black one's got something wrong with his back legs.'

Stupid woman! There was nothing wrong with my back legs. It wasn't my fault that Woody and my mother had funny blobby things on the end of theirs. They popped us into the box and we dived under a blanket, shivering and scrabbling in a desperate attempt to escape. Woody piddled all over my head and later claimed that I'd bitten his ear, but there were no witnesses and I deny everything.

Mum was beside herself, of course, and was rushing round mewing and growling. We heard later that she'd worked herself up into such a state that she'd flung herself into the metal trap thing by mistake and been taken into the care of something called Cats Protection. If snatching poor defenceless cats and kittens comes under the heading of "protection", heaven help us!

Woody and I were carted off as well to be looked after by a Cats Protection fosterer. Horrible though it was living down the side of that old shed, I began to feel quite nostalgic about it as we jolted along in that awful noisy old car. Woody perked up and adopted a relentlessly cheerful approach which forced me to slap his silly tabby face.

'I think they're taking us somewhere really good,' he chirruped, 'with lots to eat and a nice warm bed.'

I gave him a withering look, which is quite hard to do when someone's got their paw in your eye, but I managed pretty well.

A short time after we had been installed in a big cage, we heard a lot of swearing and screaming and recognised Mum's voice. She shot out of the trap, catapulted into the cage and promptly smacked both of us in the face as if the whole episode had been our fault! Woody said she was over-emotional and it might be hormones. I resolved then and there to give hormones a wide berth if that's what they did.

A couple of weeks went by and it became obvious that Mum had something on her mind that didn't involve us. She started making strange cooing noises and rolling about with a dreamy look on her face. I asked Woody if he thought she was ill.

'I think she's what they call "in season",' he whispered. 'I overheard that woman saying that she was ready to be "spayed" – whatever that might mean.'

A week or so later, we were all waiting for our breakfast, but when the woman appeared she was carrying the large box thing and no food. She grabbed Mum and banged her up in the box, apologising to her as she did so, then whisked back in to give us our breakfast. When Mum came back later that day she was spitting feathers and had a scar on her side. Her fur had been shaved and she seemed pretty fed up.

Soon after that, some people came to look at Mum and said they would love her to come and live with them, so off she went and that was the last we saw of her.

The person fostering us was a kindly soul and was concerned that we might be missing Mum. I suppose we were, but there were so many new things to think about – and so much eating to be done – that we really didn't think too much about her.

All the Cats Protection people seemed fascinated by us and by me in particular. They kept lifting me up and examining my little back legs and mumbling about not quite knowing what the future would hold. I suppose they were a bit overwhelmed by my good looks and youthful charm.

Anyway, we were taken to see the vet and this was where Woody's increasingly irritating optimism took a bit of a knock. For a start there were two smelly, noisy creatures in the waiting room who were quite keen to eat us; our fosterer explained that they were dogs and not to be taken seriously. There was a sack on the ground too and it suddenly started moving about which freaked those dogs out I can tell you! Apparently it was something called a python and its owner said it had a very affectionate nature, but tended to become over-excited at the vet's. Eventually it was our turn to go into the consultation room where a young woman pulled us about and inspected us to the point of embarrassment. She seemed unnaturally keen to establish that we both had two round things under our tails.

'All present and correct!' she chirped, 'which is more than can be said for the black one's feet. I'm not sure how much of a future he's got, to be quite honest.'

The Cats Protection lady cuddled me and suggested to the vet that there might be a need to talk things over once she'd put us back in the car. 'I don't want the kitten to be upset,' she said, and kept kissing me. I was beginning to feel quite panicky and Woody's incessant purring was really getting on my nerves so I kicked him in the stomach with my extremely strong and normal back legs.

I don't know exactly what the conversation was that took place between our foster mum and the vet, but life continued pleasantly enough. Woody did tell me that he'd overheard two Cats Protection ladies talking and one kept saying that she thought she knew someone who would be prepared to take on a disabled kitten.

'So where's this disabled kitten, Woody?' I asked, pausing mid-munch.

He jumped up and stared at me. 'It's you, bruv!' he said, 'you haven't got any paws on your back legs, in case you hadn't noticed! And they call you "Stumpy" – there's a clue there, mate!'

Well! To be quite honest, I hadn't given it much thought. I mean, I'd obviously seen the ends of my back legs when washing my bottom, but I thought I was the normal one and it was quite a shock to realise there was something lacking. It wasn't so much the missing paws that were the problem; the more awkward thing was that my right back leg was considerably shorter than the left one. Still, I'd perfected the art of scooting along on three legs from an early age and as I became stronger I found I could manage quite well on the front two for short distances, which fascinated the old cat fosterer.

As for being called "Stumpy", it was certainly no sillier than "Woody". Most people hearing that would have expected to meet a feathery thing with a beak like a pneumatic drill.

Woody and I had just about forgotten about the first trip to the vet's when we found ourselves back there "to be adjusted" as the fosterer so sweetly put it. The day passed in a bit of a blur, but suffice it to say that by the time we left, my back paws weren't the only things that were missing.

Neither Woody nor I were very keen on being handled, so the fosterer spent a lot of time with us, tweaking mousey toys and throwing ping pong balls. Although Woody was quicker than me I found all sorts of ways of outwitting him and if all else failed I'd hang on to him so he couldn't move. Sometimes, the woman would pick us up and stroke us and although we did our best to wriggle free, we found we quite enjoyed it – just for a few seconds. When we'd had enough we'd start growling and raking at her fingers, but she kept on doing it because she said we had to be "socialised" or we wouldn't be able to be homed.

A very glamorous lady arrived one day and said she'd fallen in love with Woody, who had really overdone the cute stuff and kept blinking at her with his little tabby head on one side. She explained that she'd already got a cat from another Cats Protection person, so she wouldn't be able to take both of us.

Within a few days Woody had gone to his new home and I was one very sulky kitten. The fosterer did her best to keep my spirits up and told me she was pretty certain that I'd be on my way soon, but the person she had in mind was making all sorts of excuses about having a very old pussycat who was quite ill and couldn't be upset by a lively young kitten bouncing all over the place.

I was bashing a ping pong ball around and feeling very sorry for myself when she came rushing up to my cage and told me the news. Apparently the poor old pussycat – an ancient Persian by the name of Boris – had departed to the Great Dirt Tray in the sky and the weird woman who had owned him was now desperate to have me.

The next day I was driven to my new home. There was nothing about the outward appearance of this extremely dull looking bungalow to warn me of the chaos that lurked within, but if I tell you that a wobbly ginger cat was enthusiastically bonking his bed when we arrived, a picture may be forming in your innocent little minds.

I was put into a cage in the corner of the lounge and after an emotional farewell my fosterer departed. I felt pretty emotional too – nothing to do with the fosterer departing, but everything to do with finding myself stuck with two mad people and an assortment of seriously weird felines who were draped over every available surface.

I soon learned that the female human was the Earth Mother – a dumpy mushroom of a woman with a face like a melon wearing glasses. The man certainly looked more normal, but was known as Poor Roger, for fairly obvious reasons.

Once I'd calmed down a bit and had a good look at the cats, I drew comfort from the fact that there only appeared to be two fairly normal ones – a huge black lump known as Count Lucio due to his rather dubious Italian origins – and a pert little black girl called Evie. The jumbled furry heap on the sofa gradually unravelled to reveal an ancient tabby coat-hanger called Bonnie Bun-Bun, a black and white creature, Miss Isabelle, who didn't seem to know what her back legs were doing and Miss Elizabeth, a white and tabby girl with a most peculiar wiggling walk.

The bed bonker turned out to be a brain-damaged teddy bear known as Benjamin Wobble, while a glance through into the dining room revealed a fluffy heap who was, apparently, a pedigree Persian who had fallen on hard times – St Petersburg Cloud Princess, pet name Bella. This strange apology for a feline seemed to live on the dining room table if the large igloo and numerous feeding bowls were anything to go by.

When I looked out of the patio door I nearly had a heart attack because I'd never realised a person could be so small. A second and more searching look revealed that it was in fact a portly tortoiseshell cat, but the resemblance to a human in a cat outfit was really quite uncanny and haunted my dreams for some time to come. This was Portia – a cat with ideas above her station who had lived most of her life as head rabbit catcher to Major Ferguson in Dummer.

Quite frankly, looking at this lot made me realise that not having hind paws was such a minor disability that it was hardly worth mentioning.

CHAPTER TWO

Settling In

I was only in the cage for a couple of days, after all those dire threats that I'd be banged up for three weeks! I came out quite cautiously because there were several sets of bloodshot eyes peering at me – including those belonging to the Earth Mother and Poor Roger. I edged round the sofa and Miss Elizabeth reached down to give me a sharp clip round the ear in her caring way, then Bonnie Bun-Bun yawned in my face and her pilchard breath very nearly rendered me unconscious.

At an early stage it became obvious that the main risk was being crushed by that ginger dollop, Benjamin Wobble, who kept following me and barging into me. Luckily, he soon noticed that there was food in my cage and clambered in there to slurp it up, leaving me free to explore my new home.

I was just poking around in one of the bedrooms and wishing my back legs didn't slip about so much on the stupid wooden floor, when loud sneezing made me jump out of my skin. I turned round in time to see Bella the Persian digging energetically at the floor prior to squatting down and peeing.

I was mesmerised by the sight of the amber liquid flowing under the bed, but old fluffy bum just sort of shrugged and wandered off.

'Won't they be cross with you for doing that?' I squeaked, but the blank look on her flat face when she turned round persuaded me that St Petersburg Cloud Princess couldn't have cared a flying fruit bat.

It soon became apparent that somebody else had taken her behaviour rather badly when the Earth Mother windmilled into the bedroom clutching a toilet roll.

'What sort of example is that to set the new boy?' she squawked. 'I really am very disappointed in you, Bella. We've got more dirt trays than most people have had hot dinners and it wouldn't hurt you to get your bottom into one occasionally!'

After scrubbing away at the floor and the Persian for several minutes, the Earth Mother disappeared and was soon to be heard berating Poor Roger.

Directing her comments at the study door, the Earth Mother reminded him that she had always thought it a bad idea to move the dirt tray from its strategic position under the bedroom window.

'Poor little Bella was so confused that she had an accident on the floor!' she snapped. 'She must have been so embarrassed having a mishap in front of Stumpy!'

'But she's always peeing on the floor!' came the muffled reply. 'I've never seen her use the dirt tray – under the window or anywhere else.'

I was soon to learn that this was the usual formula for the apportionment of blame at Tresta Towers. Whatever happened, it would end up being Poor Roger's fault even if he was out of the country at the time. I once heard her telling a girlfriend about a car accident she'd had before they were married, when Poor Roger was still happily ensconced in his cosy pad in Bristol and she was terrorising the population – human and feline – in the leafy lanes of Surrey. When the car finally came to rest on its side in a ditch, the first thing the Earth Mother did was to phone Poor Roger and blame him for the accident.

'But I'm a hundred miles away!' he protested feebly.

'Exactly!' shrieked the Earth Mother triumphantly, 'if you'd been up here driving the bloody car it obviously wouldn't have happened!'

I was still rummaging around in the bedroom when Evie appeared in the small top window, swaying dangerously before crashing down on the windowsill and knocking a plant pot for six. It was quite an entrance and the Earth Mother came thundering through again to stare helplessly at the mess.

'I do wish you wouldn't do that, Evie!' she twittered, 'poor Stumpy must wonder what sort of home he's come to!'

It was clear from Evie's measured stride and nonchalant tail flicks that this sort of thing was pretty routine. She sauntered past me as I cowered in the corner, delivering a well-judged spit right between my eyes. I was quite fascinated by this vision of feline loveliness and decided to overlook the fact that she seemed to be worryingly normal. In fact, I resolved there and then to ask her if she would like to be my new mother, but this was obviously something that would need to wait until she was in a more maternal frame of mind. Eventually, I gave up waiting and asked her anyway. She looked at me in amazement and mumbled something about waiting to see if a normal kitten turned up – which seemed a bit harsh and not all that likely at Tresta Towers.

Scooting through to the kitchen, I met up with Miss

Isabelle who was poking about at some cat food. Feeling a bit peckish, I launched myself at the plate and started tucking in, only to be knocked across the floor by her small, but surprisingly powerful, white paw.

'I thought you didn't want it,' I squeaked.

'I didn't until you started stuffing your face,' she replied sweetly.

As time went on I soon learned that Miss Isabelle could gossip for Woking. Never one to let the facts get in the way of a good story, Miss Isabelle had achieved some notable triumphs – including persuading the other residents that the crash made by a falling tree was in fact the Earth Mother tripping over Benjamin Wobble. This was obviously a load of old pussy poo as the crash would have been much louder if the Earth Mother had indeed plummeted. Isabelle was the airhead who some time ago thought that Jess was a completely different creature from Geoffrey because the Earth Mother had sneakily changed his name; she also famously concluded that when Bella the Persian arrived, she was actually Calico who had passed away some months previously. Apparently, according to Miss Isabelle, Calico had just been out in the garden for rather a long time and when she came back in her face was much flatter than when she went out because she'd had an argument with a wall.

My first encounter with the spaniel-sized cat known as Count Lucio perked me up considerably. He stared at me, knocked me over and rolled me around on the carpet, then kicked me in the head in the most affectionate way imaginable. I squealed my head off and the Earth Mother rushed in flapping a tea towel.

'Lucio! Leave that poor kitten alone this minute! Poor baby! He must be terrified!'

Actually, I was having a wonderful time because I'd really missed the rough play fights I used to have with Woody and – leaving aside the fact that Lucio was black and about ten times the size of my little tabby brother – it was just like old times.

The cage was dismantled within days of my arrival and soon I felt I'd never lived anywhere else. The Earth Mother and Poor Roger were very over-protective and wouldn't let me out into the garden, which was annoying, but I suppose they meant well, which is about the most damning thing anyone could say about anybody.

Apparently they were worried about me being eaten by a fox and, when they weren't worrying about that, they were worrying about the ends of my back legs getting sore on the cold ground. Their plan was that I would stay indoors until after the winter, but it certainly wasn't mine.

Everything was ticking along pleasantly when Count Lucio went missing. The big black lump was gone for three days before being found in next door's garden more dead than alive. An anxious time followed, with poor old Lucio banged up at the vet's and subjected to visits from the Earth Mother and Poor Roger. As if he wasn't suffering enough! They used to take in tempting little meals which he shunned, preferring to lurk behind his dirt tray. Being slightly challenged in the height department, the humans had to stand on boxes of cat food to reach him. I could only begin to imagine the horror experienced by that poor cat as their podgy fingers wiggled over the horizon.

After a week or so, Count Lucio was referred to a specialist in deepest Kent, wherever that might be, and off they tootled down the M25 with our hero reclining in a large carrier on the back seat. The Earth Mother was slightly miffed about this celebrity treatment as she had been waiting for months on the old NHS list to have some fairly trivial operation.

Apparently, Count Lucio was the only non-pedigree animal in the waiting room, which was awash with perfumed pooches and cosseted cats. Relying heavily on his Italian charm, Lucio showered the vet with kisses and the poor woman was instantly putty in his rather large paws.

After having every test known to man and cat, a cordon bleu supper and a sleepover, Count Lucio decided he felt considerably better and returned home to be poked in the eye by Miss Elizabeth.

Soon after this, the Earth Mother suddenly disappeared for a couple of days, but nobody made any effort to look for her. As Isabelle said, it was just like her to go away for a luxurious little break when we were running short of freshly cooked chicken. Eventually we heard she was lazing around in hospital, but it wasn't all bad because Poor Roger was so busy visiting the selfish woman that we had plenty of time to ourselves. We were all dozing away on the third afternoon when the phone rang and we heard Poor Roger saying, 'This afternoon? What – today? I was going down the road to get some cat litter!'

There was some fairly manic squeaking at the other end and a couple of hours later off he went, to return with the Earth Mother who appeared to be walking on stilts. She was quite tired and emotional when she first arrived home, but this happy state of affairs didn't last long and she was soon directing operations from a cushion-stacked chair in the middle of the lounge.

Poor Roger was just a blur as he rushed between the lounge and the kitchen, while the Earth Mother commandeered the remote control for the telly and issued orders on a random basis. Miss Isabelle said she'd had a replacement hip; why they didn't replace some of the more visible parts while they were at it, I really don't know.

Anyway, within hours she was soon mobile enough on those stilt things to make everybody's life a misery. Bonnie Bun-Bun did her best to unbalance her by weaving – at speed – between the stilts, but there was no stopping the Earth Mother once she'd gathered momentum. The next day, intent on going for the sympathy vote, she ventured round the block and one or two neighbours who didn't dodge back indoors quickly enough ended up hearing more than they could possibly have wanted to know about the seeping wounds and recalcitrant bowels of the woman in the opposite bed.

The most entertaining aspect of the Earth Mother's convalescence was the donning of the white elastic stockings which she was required to wear at night. Poor Roger – already exhausted by the daunting number of tasks undertaken during these very long days – would meet this final challenge with a mixture of hysteria and desperation. As he dragged on these impossibly tight stockings – on to the Earth Mother's legs I mean, not his own – a vigorous tug would see the Earth Mother's head banging against the headboard of the bed like a spiky battering ram and removing them often had her perilously draped over the foot of the bed while Poor Roger struggled manfully with concussion after an altercation with the wardrobe door.

While the humans were having all this fun, we had to make the best of things and I found myself bonding with Count Lucio and Miss Evie. Being so large, Lucio caused havoc indoors when in playful mode and the Earth

Mother would nearly fall off her pile of cushions as she lunged at the flying black cannonball.

'If you're going to behave like a supercharged Shetland pony, you can go outside!' she shrieked. Count Lucio just looked at her in amazement and got as close to shrugging his shoulders as a cat can get when travelling through a cluttered lounge at the speed of sound.

Evie and Lucio were definitely becoming a bit of an item, it seemed. It was the way she spat at him that gave the game away. He'd chase her into the depths of the wardrobe and she would pretend to be scared, but that didn't fool me. She wasn't particularly pleasant to me at first, but after a while she realised I made a more interesting playmate than the other residents of the Special Needs Unit and started to share the remains of her mice with me. I say remains, because Evie enjoyed nothing more than ripping them apart and distributing the innards at various levels. A particularly tasteful arrangement of tails and ears dangled from the top of the wall unit for some months before the domestic goddess stirred herself sufficiently to remove it.

I soon realised that the Earth Mother and Poor Roger had a whole coachload of cronies who were every bit as weird as they were. As soon as the news broke that I was in residence, a steady stream of callers beat a path to the door, squealing with delight and scooping me up for cuddles and kisses. I could have done without these unseemly displays of emotion, but the toys they brought were worth having.

One very glamorous lady asked the Earth Mother if she could be my godmother. Instead of just saying "yes" or "no", the Earth Mother felt the need to introduce a note of competition and told Patricia that lots of people were clamouring for the honour. This had the effect of making

Patricia quite desperate and she started talking about taking responsibility for choosing the right school and changing my name to "Sebastian" because she didn't think "Stumpy" would open the right doors! See what I mean? Mad as a box of frogs, all of them!

I should have known that other members of the team would feel the need to draw attention to themselves when they realised I was becoming something of a celebrity, and it wasn't long before Benjamin Wobble started getting in on the act. I'd heard the Earth Mother and Poor Roger rambling on about him having fits and hadn't had a clue what they were talking about – no change there, of course – until floppy old Benjamin suddenly went all peculiar before my very eyes.

It goes without saying that it was the Earth Mother's fault. She was off the stilts by this time, but still a bit restricted in the bending department so had assembled a collection of deeply unattractive shoes with Velcro fastenings. This particular evening, the old dear collapsed in a heap and wrenched at the Velcro fastenings with rather more vigour than usual. It was a fairly dreadful noise by any standard, but Benjamin was beside himself. He shot out of his bed and raced round in ever-decreasing wobbly circles, eventually flinging himself behind the sofa where he remained for some minutes.

The Earth Mother and Poor Roger were devastated, burbling away about the need to time the fit in case action was needed. A frantic rummage ensued for the "rectal diazepam", resulting in a landslide of carrier bags and other treasures from what is frighteningly termed "the emergency cupboard". Never mind the diazepam bit – the mention of "rectal" is enough to make anybody's eyes water and Benjamin emerged from his hiding place at precisely the same moment as the Earth Mother rushed in clutching a crumpled bag. It turned out that she'd picked up the one containing clothes pegs, but it had the desired effect and Benjamin wasn't taking any chances. I noticed he sat down rather abruptly as she approached, tucking his tail between his legs.

Later that evening, the great ginger dollop was lolling about on Poor Roger's lap as usual and the Earth Mother suddenly did one of her "Benjy" voices, because – apparently – Benjamin was talking. I couldn't hear any pearls of wisdom, so I climbed on to the sofa to peer into his face. All the great lump was doing was opening and closing his mouth and dribbling in a pathetic and revolting manner.

The Earth Mother and Poor Roger were entranced. 'Benjy's talking!' marvelled the Earth Mother, stroking his head. 'What's Benjy Boo saying? Is Benjy saying he loves Mummy and Daddy?'

At first I was quite worried about their behaviour, but I soon realised they were besotted with all of us. I also comforted myself with the thought that the bozos who suddenly lose the plot and mow down lots of innocent people are always described by their neighbours and friends as boring and inconspicuous. Applying this logic, I felt safe in assuming that any mass murders in our little cul-de-sac would inevitably be carried out by the extremely pleasant and sensible neighbours who are pillars of the residents' association and always put out the right dustbin on the right day.

CHAPTER THREE

It's a Wild World

A great sadness descended on Tresta Towers when dear old Portia Patch suddenly started walking away from the food bowls when there were still some yummy morsels waiting to be consumed. The Earth Mother and Poor Roger gathered up the feisty old sausage and rushed off to the vet's, but nothing could be done and Portia was brought home to be indulged and petted until it was her time to go. As it happened, within days the vet had to be called to ease poor old Portia's departure to the Great Dirt Tray in the sky.

Portia made the most of her moment by deciding to linger over her last meal, watched by the vet, the nurse, the Earth Mother and Poor Roger. When the time came, our once-portly "person in a catsuit" slipped away easily. Perhaps she could already see the angelic rabbits on the Elysian fields of Dummer Downs and was running through the grass to give those bunnies a run for their money.

Portia and Bonnie Bun-Bun had been companions for many years, long before they were brought to Tresta Towers, and the humans were worried that the ancient tabby coat-hanger would be devastated when she realised Portia had left us. Having dribbled the afternoon away on the humans' bed, Bun-Bun arrived in the kitchen as we were gathering for supper and reviewed the situation with her cobwebby old eyes. Hoisting in that Portia was absent from our midst, she shook her head, yawned and was tucking into a heap of Kittydins before the plate had hit the deck.

The Earth Mother was determined to have a drama and proclaimed that Bun-Bun was simply comfort eating, but it looked horribly like greediness from where I was standing. Later that evening, Bun-Bun could be seen snuggling up to Elizabeth, clasping Lizzie's white and tabby body in her skinny old paws and snoring a spluttery snore into her ear. The Earth Mother and Poor Roger were entranced, but something about Lizzie's tight-lipped expression suggested that she had some way to go before sisterly bonding would be achieved. At one point – somewhere between *University Challenge* and *Midsomer Murders* – Elizabeth gave vent to her emotions with a low growl, but Bun-Bun, being stone deaf, felt the vibration and assumed that her friend was purring. As the tabby's paws tightened round her friend's stomach, we all realised that Lizzie didn't stand a chance.

By this time, we were lurching into February and the Earth Mother was toying with the idea of letting me out. Unfortunately, this toying took rather a long time, but eventually the patio door was left open and out I went. I took my time venturing over that green stuff and at first the cold dampness was a bit of a shock. The ends of my back legs had calloused over, but were still quite sensitive compared to my front paws. As I went down the garden, I noticed the wild girls, Delilah and Spitfire, skulking in the bushes. I hadn't met them before because they lived outside, but I was used to seeing them through the patio door.

Delilah – the fluffy tortoiseshell number with coquettish white snowshoes – bobbed out to sniff noses before slapping me round the face, while Spitfire – a scary-looking panther of a cat – just spat and growled in the friendliest manner possible as she rushed past and knocked me for six. Miss Isabelle had told me about a black and white wild girl called Pansy, who turned up in the front garden for food several times a day and was, to quote Miss Isabelle, over-indulged to a ridiculous extent by the Earth Mother and Poor Roger. This being the case, Miss Isabelle had made it her business to chase Pansy off at every opportunity.

I was just dithering about when I saw a squirrel twitching its way down the pine tree a few feet away. When it saw me it flung a stream of squirrelly swear words in my direction and jerked its tail about in what I suppose was meant to be a gesture of defiance. Well, I did my best, but as soon as I moved towards it, the sneaky creature leapt up the tree, chattering to itself and kicking an avalanche of pine needles down on my head. I resolved to wreak terrible revenge on Mr Ratty-Chops at the earliest opportunity.

Another cause of excitement was a low-flying pigeon which screeched to a ragged halt on the patio table and proceeded to tuck into the remains of the wild girls' breakfast. I rushed back up the garden and had a wonderful view of its bulging feathery belly as I crouched under the glass table. Old Spitfire came from nowhere and frightened Percy Pigeon almost to death; it didn't do a lot for me either, so I scampered back indoors to be gathered up by the Earth Mother, who told me I was a little hero.

As the weather warmed up, I spent more and more time in the garden. One day I turned round to glimpse the vision of loveliness otherwise known as Bella, St Petersburg Cloud Princess, teetering on the steps into the garden. Do you know, I had quite forgotten that the creature had legs as she spent nearly all her time in her igloo on the dining table. Watching her tottering along on those knobbly little pins made me realise – yet again – that my slight deficiency is but a tiny blip on the great computer screen of life.

Even Bonnie Bun-Bun occasionally ventured into the garden, wandering in circles and wailing to the extent that we expected the RSPCA inspector to turn up any minute. Miss Elizabeth did her best to jolly the old sausage along, but it was the promise of another meal that usually lured her back indoors. Poor old Bun-Bun was completely deaf, but the Earth Mother had perfected a bizarre form of sign language which seemed to convey something to Bun-Bun, but provided further evidence of insanity to onlookers.

When communicating with the ancient tabby, the Earth Mother would crouch down, nudge Bun-Bun to attract her attention and do an exaggerated eating mime, accompanied with tummy rubbing. Bun-Bun would peer at her intently and skip towards the kitchen where a running buffet would hold her attention for at least ten seconds before she wandered off, howling to the skies, the squirrels and the occasional visiting woodpecker.

By now, I had achieved several triumphs on the hunting field, including nailing a particularly uppity slug and a blundering butterfly. The slug had it coming because he was slithering up the patio door and I hope the smack I gave him made him think twice about doing it again. The butterfly was clearly terrified when it realised that the mighty black hunter had it in his sights, but managed to elude capture by fluttering into the "conservation area" – an extensive weed-filled wasteland at the bottom of the garden.

One morning, as I was popping indoors for a small snack, I heard the Earth Mother and Poor Roger chatting – or the Earth Mother chatting and Poor Roger contributing the occasional grunt.

'That lovely lady that adopted Whisky has died,' said the Earth Mother. 'You remember Whisky – the black and white girl with three legs.'

Poor Roger, who was engrossed in his latest photographic magazine, looked up briefly and gave a facial twitch that could have been a smile or – more probably – wind.

'Yes – so I'm just going round to collect her. Won't be long!'

At this point, the magazine fell from Poor Roger's trembling hands. 'Why are you collecting the cat?' he asked, while Elizabeth and Isabelle smirked on the sofa.

The Earth Mother sighed in an exaggerated manner. 'Because, dear, I'd promised to give Whisky a home if ever anything happened to her owner. Well, obviously something has happened because the poor woman has died.'

'But you've retired from Cats Protection now!' ventured Poor Roger, 'surely the cat could be taken in and re-homed by them?'

The Earth Mother smiled and spoke very slowly and clearly. 'The point is that I gave a personal promise to take Whisky,' she said in a slightly menacing tone, 'and I am not the sort of person who goes back on a promise.'

Exasperation finally overwhelmed Poor Roger. 'How

many more cats have you promised to take, for God's sake? You'll probably turn up with a car load of prisoners next!'

This last remark was a not very subtle reference to the Earth Mother's recent volunteering efforts at the local prison. By now, Elizabeth and Isabelle were beside themselves with delight, presumably having witnessed this sort of thing on numerous occasions.

Possibly deciding that right was not entirely on her side, the Earth Mother rapidly adopted the "never apologise, never explain" policy that I would soon learn formed a key element in her strategy.

'I haven't got time now to bandy words,' she said, heading purposefully towards the door with a cat carrier. 'Perhaps you could just put the kitten pen up and sort out some food and a bed... ?'

The door slammed and we all looked at Poor Roger, who retrieved his magazine and made a spirited effort to immerse himself in the intricacies of exposure and magnification before flinging it down and striding across the garden to fetch the kitten pen from the summerhouse. By the time the Earth Mother returned with a cross-looking black and white cat, all was in readiness. Within minutes Poor Roger was on his hands and knees telling Whisky that she was safe now and if she didn't like the minced chicken he would cook her some fish.

I would like to say that the new arrival was grateful and loving, but she was actually a right old bag and showed precious little sign of responding to any overtures of friendship from the rest of us. Miss Elizabeth was anxious to make Whisky aware of her own Head Monitor status, but Whisky seemed conspicuously unimpressed if the gaping yawn was anything to go by. Benjamin Wobble viewed her as another bonking prospect and spent long hours crouching by the kitten pen, all to no avail unless her "Disgusted of Tonbridge Wells" expression was an inverse indicator of simmering passion.

I had an experimental poke at her catnip mouse, which was tantalisingly close to the edge of the pen, but Whisky nearly removed my front paw and I retreated hurriedly as I couldn't really afford to lose another one. St Petersburg Cloud Princess and Bonnie Bun-Bun remained totally disinterested in the newcomer, mainly because neither had realised she was there. Count Lucio and Evie did realise she was there, but were far too busy fighting, hunting and playing to bother with a boring three-legged cat in a cage. After a few days, Miss Isabelle was convinced that Whisky had always been there: proof, if proof were needed, that her mother had been right to reject her at an early age.

The Earth Mother and Poor Roger were besotted with Whisky who, after resolutely ignoring all overtures, eventually admitted defeat and purred. A good couple of weeks passed before they opened the door of the pen and Whisky hopped out into the lounge. After another week or so they opened the patio door and Whisky wandered into the back garden.

'At least we know she won't be able to climb out of the garden,' mused the Earth Mother, as Whisky poked at a few pine cones and rummaged in the borders. An hour or so later, the Earth Mother wandered off, returning to see Whisky hopping up and down by the back fence like a small piebald lion.

'Roger! Roger! Whisky's going to scale the fence!' she screamed.

With commendable speed, Poor Roger galloped across the garden and grabbed Whisky round the waist as she wobbled at the top of the six foot wooden fence. Count Lucio, who later took full credit for sabotaging Whisky's escape attempt, was sitting astride the fence a few feet away.

'Hold on to her!' shrieked the Earth Mother, as Poor Roger struggled to remove Whisky's talons from his shirt and skin. 'She mustn't get away – she'll get lost, I know she will!'

I noticed two things after this worrying little episode: the first was that the newcomer was banged up for another few weeks before being released into the garden; the second was that her name suddenly changed to "Whizzy", for fairly obvious reasons.

Eventually, Whizzy was allowed out again and within minutes was seen hopping along the six foot fence. The Earth Mother spent an hour or so agonising about the possibilities of Whizzy falling into the drainage ditch behind the fence, or tumbling into a holly bush, or even plummeting into a badger sett and being chewed up by Brillo and Moonbeam, but in the end she decided that Whizzy wasn't quite as vulnerable as she had previously thought and left her to it. Unsurprisingly, as soon as the Earth Mother stopped worrying about her, Whizzy came down and sat on the lawn as if butter wouldn't melt in her furry little chops.

Apparently Whizzy had lost her hind leg in a road traffic accident when she was little more than a kitten. The Earth Mother was fond of making tasteless jokes about

Whizzy being a reckless driver, failing to notice that Whizzy was nursing murderous thoughts in her little piebald head. In fact it wasn't long before Whizzy showed what she was capable of – no, she didn't actually murder the Earth Mother, but it was a salutary warning, or would have been if the Earth Mother could have seen beyond the obvious.

It was a warm afternoon and several of us were sprawled out in the lounge by the open patio door. The Earth Mother and Poor Roger were on the sofa watching some horror programme about vets and Whizzy was outside on the patio.

'Look at little Whizzy!' cooed the Earth Mother, 'she's watching that squirrel at the bottom of the pine tree, bless her!'

Mr Ratty-Chops was certainly pushing his luck with tail twitches galore and lots of squirrelly swear words.

'I expect he knows he's safe because Whizzy's only got three legs,' chirruped the Earth Mother, drawing heavily on her vast experience of squirrel psychology.

As the words died on her lips, the three-legged cat in question streaked across the lawn and chased the squirrel into the tasteful clutter of pots near the bottom of the tree.

'Goodness, little Whizzy was just a blur!' observed the Earth Mother. 'Still, she'll never catch him amongst all those pots. Squirrels are so agile!'

Seconds later, Whizzy sauntered out with the squirrel clamped in her jaws. Glancing round to make sure of her audience, she gave the hapless rodent a sharp shake and dropped him. After prodding the corpse for a moment or two, our plucky little huntress retired to the bushes to smooth her whiskers.

It was a stylish performance by any standard and I felt a grudging admiration for our three-legged friend. I said as much to Cloud Princess when the latter descended from the dining room table to piddle regally and copiously over the bedroom floor, but the old mop-head just stared at me with those huge round eyes and said she couldn't understand why anybody would want to run after things when they could sit in an igloo and wait for the humans to fill up their food bowl.

'But it's what cats do!' I squeaked, 'it's a matter of pride!'

Whizzy's triumph made me more determined than ever to be a successful hunter and I was thrilled when Evie brought me mice to chase. Lucio and Evie would watch me with proud looks on their faces, while the Earth Mother and Poor Roger rushed around trying to rescue the mice. When they did manage to scoop one up, they would be overwhelmed with guilt because they had upset me – but not so overwhelmed that they would let me have it back, of course.

One evening the Earth Mother came thundering in from the garden to grab her "picky-uppy" thing. This handy gadget was something she had purchased to help her reach things in the dark days of the hip replacement, and long after the need had passed she used it to make our lives a misery. She would swoop on tasty morsels like chicken bones and dead moths just as we were about to cram them into our mouths, in an extremely irritating and unsporting manner. Anyway, on this occasion the wretched woman launched forth towards the summerhouse, armed with "picky-uppy". She proceeded to reach up and cast about the roof until Poor Roger was moved to ask what the hell she was trying to do.

'There's a paper bag up on the roof – I'm trying to get it down. I would have thought it was obvious!'

It might have been a good idea if it had been a paper bag, but unfortunately it was Whizzy whose black bits couldn't be seen in the fading light.

CHAPTER FOUR

Blips on the Great Computer Screen of Life

Rumours were circulating that the Earth Mother and Poor Roger were about to disappear from our midst for one of their little cruises. At first I thought we would be left to the not-so-tender-mercies of Miss Elizabeth in her head monitor role, but Benjamin Wobble said there was no need to worry because a nice person known as Auntie K would be coming to look after us. In cat speak, of course, "nice" generally equates to "pushover", so this news perked me up considerably.

Several things gave the game away, including the volume of clothes being crammed into the belly of the ancient washing machine; another indicator was the desperate search for "respectable" bedding for Auntie K as she would be staying with us. Quite what constituted "respectable" bedding, I failed to establish, but I had a shrewd idea that the usual heap of cat-shredded stuff that usually covered the humans' comatose and podgy forms didn't quite tick the box.

The day before they were due to depart, Poor Roger was out attending to various errands when the Earth Mother came bounding in from a last minute shopping spree and flung herself at a cupboard door. Apparently, while wandering aimlessly round the local supermarket, the idea had dawned that it would save time in the morning if she extracted the passports from their hiding place. As usual, a heap of miscellaneous junk cascaded across the floor. Kicking it deftly to one side, the Earth Mother reached for the documents folder where the passports were always kept. Triumphantly snatching out Poor Roger's passport and pausing only to snigger at the photograph, she reached into the folder to retrieve her own. If only it had been there.

About an hour later, Poor Roger returned and assumed there had been a burglary as the Earth Mother had rooted through forests of folders and envelopes, throwing them over every available surface. She had even snatched up my vaccination certificate and for a wild moment I pictured her trying to board the ship, sporting whiskers and black pointy ears. Surely she wouldn't have chopped her feet off? Close to tears, the Earth Mother turned on Poor Roger and accused him of removing her passport and putting it somewhere else, but he was having none of this.

'You'll have to go up to London and get a replacement,' he said briskly, 'and hopefully you'll get down to Southampton before the ship sails. If not, you'll have to fly out and join the ship at Bergen...'

'Where will you be then?' wailed the Earth Mother.

'Well obviously I'll have to go down to Southampton to board the ship with the luggage. That'll be one less thing for you to worry about.'

Another hour jerked by with Poor Roger making phone calls to the Passport Office and the Earth Mother fruitlessly rummaging in the refrigerator. At last, Poor Roger picked up the folder where the passports always were and found the Earth Mother's passport exactly where it should have been. Weak with relief, she clung to the hero of the moment and we all breathed again.

It was much later in the day when the Earth Mother suddenly turned on Poor Roger and accused him of taking the whole episode rather too calmly.

'You were in such a state, somebody had to behave sensibly!' he retorted with some justification.

'I just think you could have been more supportive – not quite so matter-of-fact about things.'

I shall gloss over the recriminations which continued way beyond suppertime, when it was embarrassingly obvious that Poor Roger's portion of lasagne was considerably smaller than the bountiful helping the Earth Mother was wedging down her own delicate throat.

I realised then that the Earth Mother and Miss Elizabeth share the same measured approach to revenge, the latter often favouring an unexpected jab in the chops days after the imagined slight has occurred.

A few weeks later, with their ocean-going adventures a spume-splattered memory, the Earth Mother and Poor Roger had embarked on various projects, each of which had to be given a grandiose title, such as "Redesigning the Garden"; this actually involved a spot of weeding and a bag of compost. Another worthy enterprise was the "Remodelling of the Bedroom"; this meant filling umpteen dustbin liners with ancient shoes and shapeless garments, destined no doubt to strike fear into the hearts of charity shop workers within a ten mile radius of Tresta Towers.

Needless to say, feelings sometimes ran high during this time of intense activity. The accidental over-pruning of a struggling clematis plant was the cause of one spirited exchange of views and the binning of a faded rock festival T-shirt another. Shortly after this last unfortunate incident, I scooted into the kitchen to find the Earth Mother amassing a frightening collection of knives and scissors on the worktop. For a moment I wondered if she was about to put an end to Poor Roger's suffering, or even to her own, but soon realised she was simply struggling to get at a new CD which appeared to be swathed in at least twenty layers of industrial strength plastic.

Being the youngest in a family of ancient and impaired felines had its advantages – particularly when it came to grabbing the choicest morsels. I soon discovered that Bella – St Petersburg Cloud Princess – was having some special and very expensive biscuits which allegedly were specially made for Persians. Talk about one being born every minute! The Earth Mother and Poor Roger are the sort of sad people that when they find themselves on a jolly outing, spend most of the time milling round pet shops or noting the location of veterinary surgeries, even though they have absolutely no intention of ever moving there.

Should they happen upon a pet shop that sells kittens, the Earth Mother makes it her business to berate the staff about the evils of encouraging people to let their cats breed when there aren't enough good homes to go round and the charities being stuffed with unwanted cats and kittens. On one of these excursions, Poor Roger noticed some Persian biscuits and brought a bag back for the mop to try. No – they hadn't actually been to Persia. The biscuits are called that because they're shaped so that flat-faced cats can get them into their badly designed mouths and thus avoid starving to death or living on porridge for the rest of their lives.

Anyway, I thought it was my duty to check these out, but getting up on the dining room table, which doubled as Princess Bella's boudoir, was quite a challenge due to the inconvenience of my missing hind paws. Still, motivated as I was by the old Persian baggage spitting like a lemonade bottle that's been dropped from a great height, I hauled myself up and tucked in. Well, those biscuits were absolutely yummy.

'Stumpy Scooter Malone! Whatever do you think you're doing?' screeched the Earth Mother, grabbing me and dumping me on the ground. 'You're about as Persian as that duster!'

She went on to accuse me of having a pointy nose and very short fur, which apart from being rather unkind, apparently made me ineligible for the spoon-shaped biscuits which had slipped down so pleasantly.

This was bad enough, but imagine my chagrin when I heard her luring that three-legged tart, Whizzy, in from the garden with promises of "special" biscuits. Snatching victory from the jaws of defeat, as one must to survive here, I concentrated on raiding both bowls at every opportunity.

By this stage I was beginning to feel that the Earth Mother and Poor Roger were taking me for granted. Apart from one little episode, when I hid under the summerhouse for a while, I had been a model pussycat, never leaving the garden and appearing promptly when called. The best bit about the summerhouse episode was that the Earth Mother became dangerously over-excited when she saw my eyes glinting in the gloom and chucked the phone down as she gathered me up. She carted me indoors and I watched gleefully as she groped about for hours in the wet grass in a desperate search for the lost phone.

It was Whizzy who made me realise it was time to rebel. She would sit on the summerhouse roof for ages while the Earth Mother and Poor Roger offered a running buffet of goodies, yawning away and washing her bottom until they despaired of ever seeing her at ground level again. Eventually, Madam Whizzy would descend and one could be forgiven for thinking the cat had overcome unimaginable odds instead of just shimmying down the yew tree and hopping across a few feet of grass to reach the patio door.

One Sunday, the humans had selfishly tootled off for a long lazy lunch, leaving us banged up indoors without so much as a decent film to pass the time. Back they came, without a hint of an apology, and graciously allowed us into the garden for a bit of a frolic before supper. A couple of hours later, they decided it was time to round us up.

'In you come, Stumpy Malone!' trilled the Earth Mother from the doorstep, while Poor Roger ventured down the garden.

'I'll clap my hands – that always brings the boy in!' said Poor Roger confidently.

Well, it might have done if I'd been in the garden, but I wasn't! I'd managed to scale the side fence by clambering up on the stone wall and hauling myself over the wooden fence into next door, so while they were calling and clapping, I was on the other side of the fence laughing my little black socks off!

The calling went on for ages, then the Earth Mother had an inspiration; she had convinced herself I was hiding under the summerhouse, so she spent the next couple of hours dangling my toy snake in what she thought were attractive wriggles and jerks. Miss Isabelle later claimed credit for providing further excitement by lurking in the bushes without showing her white feet, so every now and then the Earth Mother would see her and think she was me. Isabelle would then bounce up, exposing her dainty little white paws and the Earth Mother would plummet back into dark despair, jiggling my snake in an increasingly desperate manner.

I soon realised that the gap under next door's side gate was wide enough for me to crawl under, so I did. Benjamin Wobble asked me why I did this as he would have been too "fritted", so I told him in no uncertain terms that a cat has to do what a cat has to do. I don't think he knew what I meant and to be honest I didn't have a clue either, but there I was in the front garden with all sorts of exciting new smells to investigate.

It was nearly eleven o'clock when Poor Roger finally decided to ignore the Earth Mother's obsessive speeches about dismantling the summerhouse and strode purposefully round to the front of the bungalow, where he enjoyed a tantalising glimpse of me sitting on the pavement a few yards away.

'Stumpy! I don't believe it! Is it really you? You *are* a clever, clever, naughty, naughty boy!' burbled our hero, lunging at me with outstretched arms.

Naturally, I did the only thing that any self-respecting cat could do and scooted off into the bushes. Within seconds I heard Poor Roger calling to the Earth Mother, who was still forlornly dangling Sidney Snake to the considerable amusement of the badgers and foxes who were gathering for their cordon bleu supper.

'The little bugger! He's here – he's run into the bushes. Little sod – wait till I get my hands on him!'

So much for the return of the prodigal son! All that fond reunion stuff didn't last long, but any thoughts of revenge had to be shelved because at that moment the moon disappeared and the ground shook in a menacing manner. It was the Earth Mother bearing down on my hideout. After a tense few minutes, Poor Roger located my sweet little currant-like eyes in the torch beam and the Earth Mother flung herself under the bushes. Once she'd got her horrible fingers on the scruff of my neck, I didn't stand a chance. She dragged me out, but then couldn't stand up, so Poor Roger had to get behind her and sort of jerk her to her feet as she clutched me to her dinosaur T-shirt. Pansy, the flirty feral, told me later that it looked quite rude, but most things look rude to Pansy.

That night I was really quite tired and could hardly summon the strength to gnaw the Earth Mother's fingers, which I usually did after about two minutes of ear-tickling and fuss.

'Poor Stumpy Malone's worn out after his big adventure,' murmured the Earth Mother drowsily, 'perhaps he won't be taken over by aliens tonight... '

This quaint reference to being taken over by aliens is how the Earth Mother describes what anybody else would recognise as perfectly normal feline behaviour. Anyway, one has one's pride and without more ado I sank my dear little pearly teeth into her fat hand.

The next morning found Poor Roger engaged in feverish activity, attaching plastic panels to the wooden fences to prevent further escapes.

'There!' he said, standing back the way humans do when they're preparing to be deafened by applause, 'that should fix the little bugger!'

Well, it wouldn't and they looked ridiculous – like some extremely cheap and inappropriately positioned solar panels. The Earth Mother seemed pleased with them, but then she was easily satisfied and presumably didn't harbour ambitions to climb into next door's garden.

A few mornings later, I was fast asleep and the burglar alarm went off. This wasn't good, but worse was to come. The Earth Mother had stumbled out of bed and opened the patio door in a blind panic because Count Lucio was demanding to go out. So mindful was she of the black blob's needs that she forgot to turn the bloody alarm off before flinging open the door. Instead of calmly walking across the room to turn the thing off, the Earth Mother lurched into a run, colliding with the coffee table and stumbling into the wall. Apparently, she was worried about Benjamin Wobble being "fritted" by the whooping siren noise, whereas it was perfectly clear to the rest of us that he could take this in his wobbly little stride, but was scared witless by the Earth Mother crashing about.

A few days later, the old girl had to go for some physiotherapy and the twelve year old child conducting the initial overhaul noticed the bruises.

'Whatever have you been up to?' he asked innocently, observing the mauve and green swirls on her flabby legs – having been trained to make polite conversation with his victims, but obviously not caring two-in-the-moon.

The Earth Mother seized her opportunity and related the burglar alarm incident in mind-numbing detail. By the time she reached the bit about Benjamin Wobble's fits, listing every ailment he had ever suffered as a kitten, I suspect the physiotherapist was beginning to worry about his pension.

When the Earth Mother retired as homing officer of the local branch of Cats Protection, Poor Roger probably breathed a sigh of relief and looked forward to years of tranquillity; he may even have imagined meals of a conventional nature appearing at regular intervals – or possibly fantasised about putting things down on dust-free surfaces. Unsurprisingly, the Earth Mother has ignored every opportunity to familiarise herself with the cooker and cleaning utensils, preferring instead to spend long hours at the keyboard, tapping out incomprehensible rubbish to inflict on the unsuspecting public.

A recent project was *Evie's Diary*. Leaving aside the fact that my new cat mother, Evie, should have had the credit for this work, we could all have done with the Earth Mother keeping her artistic endeavours under wraps instead of inflicting them on the rest of us. The night before the first copies of the book were due to arrive, the Earth Mother managed to convince herself that it would be printed as *Evie's Dairy*. My own suffering was as nothing – if you discount falling off the bed twice – but Poor Roger looked as if he'd spent an hour in the ring with a mountain gorilla by the time he tottered out to make the morning cuppa. As he remarked to Benjamin, "for better or for worse is all very well, but I had hoped there would be *some* better bits… "

CHAPTER FIVE

The Dark Side

I hadn't been at Tresta Towers long before I realised that a great many strange things happened here. One morning, for example, Miss Isabelle came rushing past me muttering about the Earth Mother's feet being on fire. I turned round nervously and saw that puffs of smoke were indeed escaping from the Earth Mother's boat-like shoes as she lurched towards me. Miss Elizabeth – who knows everything – had the explanation trembling on her thin lips even as Isabelle and I hurled our fragile little bodies against the patio door.

'The old girl overdid the talcum powder this morning,' she sniggered, 'and she's pretty fed up with Poor Roger for making all those "hotfoot" jokes.'

There was a tendency for one crisis to follow another in rapid succession, so that the occasional oasis of calm found one nervously anticipating the next panic. There was rarely long to wait. We had hardly recovered from the worry about the Earth Mother's feet when a more serious episode had us reaching for Benjamin's stand-by supply of diazepam.

This time the panic concerned the pretty, but brainless feral, Delilah. Nobody could ever have accused the Earth Mother or Poor Roger of being the sharpest syringes in the surgery and it took them a while to compare notes and

41

realise that they hadn't clapped eyes on the silly creature for three days. Before you reach for the RSPCA's emergency number, I must explain that the ferals always made much of being "wild" and were inclined to wander off every now and then.

Anyway, there followed the usual half hour of total panic, interspersed with tears and recriminations, before they actually launched forth to search for the silly creature. Poor Roger was in our back garden rummaging in the undergrowth when he heard mewing noises coming from next door.

It is to our neighbours' credit that they have survived living next door to the Earth Mother for well over thirty years, showing qualities of fortitude and forbearance that should qualify them for instant beatification when the time comes. Their behaviour on this occasion was faultless and soon I could hear the Earth Mother and Poor Roger delving about on the other side of the fence. Predictably, the mewing ceased as soon as they got there and Poor Roger decided to extend the search into the woods behind. The Earth Mother stood rooted to the spot – mainly, I suspect, because she couldn't think what else to do.

After a while, some faint scrabbling noises reached her ears and she bellowed over the fence where Poor Roger was busily hacking down branches.

'Roger! I can hear some noises! I think it's her! I'm climbing up the bank!'

The last few words were almost lost in a flurry of falling rocks, a loud plop followed by "bugger" confirming that the old girl had indeed slipped down the rockery taking a charming array of microscopic alpine plants with her.

Undaunted, the Earth Mother scrambled back up and uncovered a slatted wooden box with telltale tufts of tortoiseshell fur sticking through at intervals. The box had become jammed under some knotted tree roots and the Earth Mother's frantic efforts failed to shift it. Calm as always, she dragged the unfortunate neighbour down the garden, screaming that Delilah might be dead or horribly maimed. In the event, of course, Delilah emerged unscathed – just very cross and hungry. And so was I because she'd made us *extremely* late with our supper.

As they took an axe to the offending box, the neighbours expressed surprise that something as knowing as a cat would get stuck like that, but obviously we weren't talking about cats in this instance: we were talking about Delilah.

After all the excitement I was more than ready for an early night and made sure I snuggled up on the humans' bed before Miss Elizabeth and Bonnie Bun-Bun decided to turn in, gaining an advantageous position across the Earth Mother's stomach. I'd just nodded off when a cacophony of voices boomed into the bedroom. Poor Roger woke up and staggered out of bed, while the Earth Mother clutched me and exclaimed dramatically that she would die before she'd let the intruders snatch her baby. Leaving aside the small matter of possibly wanting to be removed from the care of somebody so obviously lacking in essential life skills, I was quite touched by this sudden manifestation of maternal feeling; I was also pretty terrified.

Seconds later, Poor Roger returned, smiling wearily.

'Benjamin was standing on the remote control,' he explained, 'and he'd turned the telly on. It was a most unsuitable programme!'

Miss Elizabeth was not amused. 'That Benjamin Wobble gets away with murder,' she hissed. 'If that was one of us, we'd be on bird food for months!'

The bedroom project, which had been suspended after the initial flurry of activity, was suddenly resuscitated and we were banished to the lounge and garden because the unfortunate men engaged to transform the humans' dingy cave into a sanctuary of light and tranquillity could not be trusted to keep the doors shut. The Earth Mother maintained that men never listened to women because they were convinced that women wouldn't ever be saying anything important. I was quite surprised she had the perspicacity to realise this.

I was quite happy in the garden, but poor old Bonnie Bun-Bun started howling like coyote because she was worried about missing lunch. This had the very satisfactory outcome of forcing the Earth Mother to totter round with a tray of goodies at regular intervals in an effort to keep the RSPCA inspector at bay and discourage projectile vomiting which tended to be Bun-Bun's way of resolving problems.

Although the Earth Mother and Poor Roger spent a long time explaining to Count Lucio that he really must keep out of the way of the busy men and not trip them up, the great black lump appeared to have ignored the "not" part of the conversation. As he could scale the side fence in one bound, efforts to contain him in the back garden were doomed to failure. Noticing that one of the men was becoming a tad irritated by Lucio's keen interest in the contents of his van, the Earth Mother suggested jauntily that he should try saying "shove off" in Italian, leaving us writhing with embarrassment on the other side of the fence.

As the day progressed, an increasing number of items had to be transported from the bungalow into the garden, including Bella the Persian's igloo, because she couldn't possibly be subjected to the enquiring gaze of squirrels and magpies. By the time the white vans had disappeared into the night, only a few patches of grass could be seen poking out between an array of multi-coloured dirt-trays and feeding bowls – not to mention an array of multi-coloured cats.

'You'll have to watch your behaviour, now they've got all that new stuff!' Miss Elizabeth informed the Persian mop – or rather, the lump of grey and orange fur sticking out of the igloo.

Bella turned round and regarded Miss Elizabeth in amazement. 'Princesses can do whatever they like, wherever they like!' she snorted. 'Dirt trays are for common cats and I have no intention of using one. If you must know, it's against my religion.'

Later, when we were dozing in front of the telly, the Earth Mother's strident tones confirmed that Bella had made full use of her royal prerogative.

'*Bella!* Whatever do you think you're doing? That pee's gone right under the new wardrobe!'

By then, of course, St Petersburg Cloud Princess had returned to her igloo and was sleeping the sleep of a very naughty Persian who couldn't have cared less.

Meanwhile, I was busy honing my hunting skills and really hadn't time for all the political intrigue which was a constant theme at Tresta Towers. Poor Roger shared my enthusiasm for the great outdoors, but luckily he didn't show a lot of interest in catching and eating things, preferring to rely on the delicious meals provided by our very own domestic goddess. As anybody who has visited us with any expectation of an edible offering will know, this was a triumph of hope over experience.

Anyway, Poor Roger and I spent many happy hours in the back garden with me lurking in the bushes and Poor Roger repeatedly lugging half a ton of photographic equipment from patio to summerhouse and back again. All was tranquillity and manly camaraderie – or should I say "camera-derie" – until a rather upsetting incident occurred involving that well-known troublemaker, Mr Ratty-Chops, the squirrel.

How was I to know that Poor Roger had been lining up the perfect shot? All I saw was old Ratty-Chops chattering away at the bottom of the pine tree just asking to be pinned to the ground and nibbled, so I sprang out and grabbed him with my sweet little paws. Unfortunately, Poor Roger became dangerously over-excited at this point and jumped to his feet (this must have taken a bit of doing as he was pretty well crushed under a battery of lenses), yelling at me in quite an upsetting manner.

'You little bugger! That would have been the perfect shot! I'd have won the competition with that!'

Well, we could all say that, couldn't we? I glared at him, because his thoughtlessness had cost me my squirrel. We were busy glaring at each other when the Earth Mother's ringing tones cut across the garden.

'Why are you shouting at that poor kitten?' she demanded. 'You know how nervous he is after that terrible start in life. Where is my poor baby?'

With that, she gathered me up and took me indoors where I munched my way through a whole dish of

Persian biscuits while the Earth Mother cooed over me and told me how brave I'd been.

I hadn't finished with Poor Roger, needless to say. It was Miss Elizabeth, our resident expert on revenge, who came up with the perfect solution.

'All you've got to do is pretend you're terrified of him,' she said, suppressing a yawn. 'He's a kindly soul and the thought that you're frightened of him will upset him more than spitting or biting ever could.'

The wisdom of the older cat! I wasted no time putting this into practice, rushing into the bushes every time Poor Roger came anywhere near me. Sorted!

Around this time there was a lot of chat about somebody's birthday party. Apparently lots of Cats Protection people would be coming and we all had to hope and pray that the weather would be good because there wouldn't be enough room to swing the proverbial cat in the bungalow. A gazebo was erected in the back garden the day before and very festive it looked in the evening sunshine.

I suppose there must be households where the hostess would be up to her armpits in flour and egg yolks before such an event, but the Earth Mother merely viewed her ill-gotten gains from Waitrose with a complacent smile and relaxed with a glass or three of her favourite El Plonko.

The day dawned with lashing rain and blocked guttering, with the brightly coloured gazebo resembling a beleaguered galleon from the lounge window. Any normal person would have been slightly thrown by the fact that partygoers would need to hire boats to navigate the rivers that had once been roads; that wouldn't have been the end of their worries either, because the cascade gushing over the doorstep of Tresta Towers threatened to carry any would-be visitors halfway down the cul-de-sac. As I may have mentioned, however, any resemblance between the Earth Mother and a normal person would have been purely coincidental.

'Well, we may have to abandon thoughts of using the gazebo,' she chirped. 'Still, it'll be nice and cosy in the lounge and we'll just pass the food round because obviously people won't be able to move about once they've sat down.'

We were all wondering where the visitors would sit when the Earth Mother said briskly: 'You cats will have to go in the bedrooms once people start arriving. You can't stay in here, sprawled out over the sofa! The birthday boy can stay here, of course!'

With that, she scooped me up and started dancing round the room. So I was the birthday boy! I just hoped that was a good thing – you could never tell with the Earth Mother.

Soon the plucky Cats Protection people started to arrive and the Earth Mother grappled with pizza boxes and bags of prepared salad to give them the feast of their dreams. Bonnie Bun-Bun helped with the food – consuming vast quantities of smoked salmon which she skilfully whipped off the biscuits being wafted around as people chatted – while Benjamin "fellded over" in doorways and generally made it almost impossible to get from lounge to kitchen in less than thirty minutes.

People kept arriving and bringing me the most amazing cat toys and treats. Yippee! I realised then that having a birthday was actually a very good thing and resolved to have as many as possible in the coming year.

Once everybody had gone, the Earth Mother rather spitefully removed some of the toys and said I would be allowed to have one at a time so I would appreciate them more. This was obviously sour grapes on her part as I'd done a lot better for my first birthday than she did for her last one. All she got was some crummy old train trip when obviously what she really wanted were lots of catnip mice and dangly spiders.

Jealousy is never an attractive emotion and I couldn't help noticing how the Earth Mother increasingly made it her business to regale my admirers with exaggerated tales of my alien behaviour. She never tired of recounting my dastardly deeds in the bedroom and the life-threatening injuries she had sustained when at her most vulnerable. Leaving aside the questionable wisdom of placing "vulnerable" and "Earth Mother" in the same sentence, it was hardly my fault if her feet twitched under the duvet, forcing me to dive down the bed. It could so easily have been a rat or a poisonous snake, but was she grateful? I shall leave you to draw your own conclusions.

CHAPTER SIX

Great Uncle Tigger

We were sliding gracefully into autumn when the trusty kitten cage was once again dragged in from the darker recesses of a crumbling outbuilding and erected in the lounge. This activity was accompanied by what I can only describe as manic cheerfulness on the part of the Earth Mother and more muted cheerfulness on the part of Poor Roger.

Benjamin Wobble was desperate to climb inside the pen and succeeded in falling in the freshly prepared litter tray, emerging to spread the contents liberally over Miss Elizabeth, who smacked him robustly and was reprimanded for her efforts.

'You really must be nicer to poor Benjy-Boo,' snapped the Earth Mother. 'He can't help it; you know he's got brain damage!'

Pausing only to glare at the Earth Mother, Miss Elizabeth swept past and gave Benjy another poke.

Minutes later the Earth Mother returned clutching a large toy rabbit and stuffed it into the pen. This was quite possibly the scariest thing that had happened since my arrival at Tresta Towers.

'Do you think the old girl's finally flipped?' I asked Evie later.

'I shouldn't worry about it!' snorted my new cat

mother, extending her slender front legs and flicking an imaginary speck of dust from one gleaming black paw. 'She's always a bit strange when she's been to the hairdresser's. Poor Roger thinks it's the fumes from the hair dye.'

Later that evening, Poor Roger could stand it no longer. Waiting till the Earth Mother had her shaky fingers wrapped round a comforting glass of El Plonko, he ventured into the unknown.

'Is there any particular reason why you've put that pink rabbit in the kitten pen?' he asked hesitantly.

The Earth Mother regarded him as one might regard somebody who had asked why houses had doors. 'It'll help the cats to get used to somebody being in the pen before Great Uncle Tigger arrives,' she explained with exaggerated patience. 'It won't be such a shock then when they look in and see him.'

'But Great Uncle Tigger isn't pink!' said Poor Roger spiritedly, 'and presumably he hasn't got ears like bananas!'

The Earth Mother smiled knowingly. 'Bananas aren't pink, dear,' she said charitably, reaching for the El Plonko bottle, 'but you're right – Uncle Tigger isn't pink either!'

We were all relieved to hear this, naturally, but I must confess to awaiting the arrival of the new boy with some trepidation. In the event, it rapidly became obvious that "new" was not the most appropriate adjective.

A couple of mornings later the Earth Mother was up earlier than usual and disturbingly elated. As another shaky rendering of "Don't Cry for Me Argentina" announced her return from feeding the ferals in the garden, we stuffed down our Kittydins and made ourselves scarce.

I was quite surprised that the Earth Mother had forgotten to arrange a Red Arrows flypast to announce the newcomer's arrival. No sooner had the pink rabbit been ejected from the kitten pen and the ginger pensioner installed than the phone began leaping up and down, with any number of "aunties" enquiring after him. Benjamin Wobble was enthralled and kept hanging on the side of the cage, purring ecstatically as the old boy spat and growled.

'He loves me!' squeaked Benjamin, 'and I love him! He's my bestest friend in all the world.'

Miss Elizabeth yawned and descended from the sofa to give the newcomer the once over. 'Another scraggy old wreck!' she observed. 'This one's well past his sell-by date!'

The Earth Mother was busily regaling Poor Roger with an account of her adventures when she'd met up with Great Uncle's Cats Protection fosterer in the vet's car park.

'And then she took a rolled up bit of kitchen roll out of her handbag and opened it. "I thought you'd want to see this!" she said and guess what? It was a fur ball. It was a particularly long fur ball, which was interesting, but I couldn't see any worms in it. I had a good poke around, obviously, and some woman who was parking her car gave me a funny look. "Get a life," I thought, "haven't you ever seen a fur ball before?" Anyway, Mary asked me if I wanted to take it, but I said she could keep it. She seemed really pleased.'

Poor Roger did a lot of nodding and smiling during this moving speech, rather obviously longing for the moment when he could safely return to the undemanding company of his computer screen.

The Earth Mother hadn't finished. 'Mary said he has some constipation problems and I wondered if it might be the medication he's on. Anyway, I don't want to overdo the laxatives – remember what happened when Bun-Bun had the runs?'

At this point Poor Roger remembered a pressing need to be elsewhere – anywhere – and scuttled out of the room, leaving the Earth Mother to her memories of that happy time.

It didn't take Tigger long to realise he'd landed on his skinny ginger paws. Within hours he was out of the kitten cage and demanding food with the best of them. The Earth Mother and Poor Roger were delighted.

'I think he'll settle in – he doesn't seem to be too worried about the others,' observed Poor Roger as Tigger barged through a group of would-be diners to claim the largest portion. 'I do hope he doesn't miss his old home too much.'

One could only admire this plucky resilience, although I suppose Great Uncle Tigger's generation were renowned for a stiff upper lip approach to life's little ups and downs. Not for them the tears and tantrums of today – but enough about the Earth Mother.

It was on day three that Tigger's constipation made itself felt, with the old cat making several unproductive visits to the dirt tray then skiing along the carpet at speed.

'Push, sweetheart! Push really hard!' exhorted the Earth Mother, crouching down beside him and making the most revolting noises.

After many anxious hours, the Earth Mother's whoop of delight announced that Tigger had lost nearly half his body weight. It was as well we were aware of the preceding drama or we might have suspected that a visiting wolfhound had made free with the facilities.

I was quite indifferent to the new arrival until I realised he was having his medication in those really yummy Webbox sticks. To add insult to injury, it wasn't long before Bonnie Bun-Bun got in on the act and the spectacle of these two pensioners doing their synchronised pill-taking drove me mad. I tried whipping the Webbox sticks away and the Earth Mother swooped on me.

'*Stumpy!*' she screamed, snatching me up, 'they are absolutely not for you! Having no back paws will be the least of your problems if you keep this up!'

Glossing over the utter tastelessness of referring to my disability in that heartless manner, it wouldn't have hurt her to give me some. I'd spent hours frightening off those birds that kept eating all our nuts and suet balls – often in appalling conditions – and had spared no effort breaking off those horrid mauve saucers on that new clematis plant.

A couple of days later, Count Lucio was chasing me round the bedroom and over the bed when he suddenly disappeared. Suspecting an ambush, I sneaked round the bed. Suddenly, Lucio leapt out of a drawer he'd pulled out and my little heart nearly stopped. The Earth Mother heard the commotion and came stampeding through, smacked her leg against the open drawer and crashed to the floor. If she was looking for sympathy, she was out of luck. Just one Webbox stick and I would have been there licking her melon-like face.

It doesn't take much to make the Earth Mother and Poor Roger happy, which is lucky really because so much of their lives revolves around vet trips and dirt tray issues.

Hardly had the Earth Mother recovered from the ecstasy of Great Uncle's tail end productivity than the postman arrived with another surprise. So delighted had the Earth Mother been with Cloud Princess' transformation from hairy beetroot to something resembling a Persian cat, that she'd written to the Persian food manufacturers extolling the virtues of their wonder product. I could imagine the reaction of the unfortunate recipient of the Earth Mother's flowery prose.

'Listen to this one, Sharon! You'd think she'd won the lottery or got a date with David Beckham! Goes on about those Persian biscuits transforming her life. Sounds like she's eating them herself!'

The Earth Mother ripped open the package and the enclosed letter, stuck it back together and read it in a state of breathlessness. She then seized the bubble-wrapped object, stabbed herself several times with the scissors and eventually held aloft a mug with Persians on it.

'Roger! Where are you? Look at this – it's the most beautiful mug with a picture of Bella! Oh – it's *so* lovely!'

She then rushed up to Bella, flaunting this newly acquired and priceless treasure, only to have the ghastly old Persian sneeze all over it.

'There you are!' cried the Earth Mother, 'Bella recognised herself on the lovely mug. She's such a clever girl!'

Looking at the flat-faced blankness that is Bella's habitual expression, I could only think that if there really was a razor-sharp intelligence buried deep inside that fuzzy little head, she had missed her vocation and MI5 would never benefit from this invaluable and discreet addition to its workforce.

Inevitably, the relative luxuriance of Bella's coat brought fresh challenges in the grooming department. During her bald beetroot days, a quick session with a soft brush would soon have the sparse tufts of fur facing in roughly the same direction, but now more rigorous efforts were required to maintain Cloud Princess as she wished her adoring public to see her. Having always worked at the "moggy end" of the market, the Earth Mother now found herself seeking guidance on how to maintain a pedigree – a pedigree with more design faults than a porous roof.

In due course a special comb was purchased and we all breathed a sigh of relief as we were heartily sick of the Earth Mother's constant ramblings on the subject. Miss Elizabeth, in her irritatingly knowing way, assured the rest of us that this was just the beginning of the rest of our pointless little lives.

In no time at all, the run-of-the-mill steel comb had become "Mr Comby" and Bella loved him more than anything. The Earth Mother would do her special "Mr Comby" voice and Cloud Princess would ping out of her igloo to be combed and cosseted, because she knew that "Mr Comby" would see off naughty "Mr Tangle".

Embarrassment levels soared when an unfortunate photographer from the local newspaper was despatched to take a photo of the Earth Mother following the publication of yet another load of cat-related rubbish. Realising that a picture of the Earth Mother clutching a book was hardly likely to set the nation's pulses racing, the photographer searched desperately for some additional sparkle. He noticed me and immediately begged me to take part in this doomed enterprise, but the

Badger

Bella

Benjamin Wobble

Bonnie Bun Bun and Elizabeth

Delilah

Evie

Great Uncle Tigger

Lucio

Miss Elizabeth

Miss Isabelle

Pansy

Portia Patch

Spitfire

Squirrel

Stumpy Malone

Whizzy

Earth Mother spitefully informed him that I didn't feature in this particular publication.

'I really think Cloud Princess would be the obvious candidate,' she trilled, attempting to lure the mop out of her igloo. 'Princess is pedigree – in fact she's the only one of us that is!'

If the photographer felt the icy hand of fear clasping his nether regions, he was man enough to put a brave face on things. His features assumed a slightly frozen look, but he assumed a kneeling position and smiled encouragingly at Bella's fuzzy trousers.

'Could she be encouraged to face the camera?' he asked in a reasonable tone.

'Oh, of course! Roger – bring Mr Comby in! Bella will do anything for Mr Comby.'

Ten minutes later, after several unfortunate smacks round the head while Poor Roger attempted to attract the mop's attention with a wildly waving Mr Comby, the photographer ventured that it might be an idea to try another model.

'We're spoilt for choice here!' giggled the Earth Mother. 'How about Benjamin Wobble? He loves being photographed.'

The evidence for Benjy's obsession with the camera was – to put it mildly – less than compelling. It's true that there were any number of photographs of the ginger lump scattered around the walls of Tresta Towers, but in most of them the Earth Mother had him pinned against her bosom in a vice-like grip so that the poor cat's eyes positively bulged.

Nothing – including steam rollers, runaway trains and nuclear explosions – was going to stop the Earth Mother and the unsuspecting Benjy didn't stand a chance. Finding himself on the dining room table, he actually stayed up the right way for all of ten seconds before rolling over and sticking his silly wobbly legs in the air.

'Bless him!' cooed the Earth Mother. 'Would it be an idea if I turned upside down as well? Then you could turn the picture the right way up afterwards.'

An hour later and having aged ten years, the photographer staggered back to his car, no doubt thinking that a lengthy spell as a war correspondent in Afghanistan would have been a stroll in the park compared to an assignment involving a mad woman and her cats in downtown Woking.

CHAPTER SEVEN

The Good, the Bad and the Deluded

I'd realised at an early stage that any relationship between the committing of a misdemeanour and the apportionment of blame at Tresta Towers was purely coincidental. Nothing, for example, would ever be the Earth Mother's fault and nothing was ever Benjamin's fault, even when caught red-pawed in the act. Nothing was ever the fault of the pointy-nosed badgers either. They could excavate the lawn, upend freshly planted pots and wipe their snotty noses over the patio door with impunity and we were all supposed to feel privileged that they had condescended to visit us.

A strangled cry from the Earth Mother when wiping badger dribbles from the patio door interrupted a rather pleasant post-breakfast snooze and I looked up to see her clutching her fingers while blood trickled down the glass. Sitting next to her with a wide-eyed look of innocence on his chubby ginger chops was none other than Benjy Boo. It appeared that Benjamin had become dangerously excited at the sight of the dangling cloth and had tried to grab it, unfortunately making contact with the Earth Mother's delicate flesh.

'Stumpy! That's your fault!' screeched the Earth Mother – a tad unreasonably, I thought. 'If you'd played with Benjy in the garden instead of ignoring him, he would never have done that!'

The sight of the fat ginger cherub's blank face made my paws twitch, but retribution often comes in unlikely forms and none more so than in the form of Miss Elizabeth, who minced over to him and gave him a good old poke as soon as the Earth Mother had disappeared to bathe her wounds.

A few days later the Earth Mother returned from the shops bursting with the news that she'd seen a man she knew very well and hadn't seen for ages. She couldn't actually remember his name, or where she knew him from, but these details were lost in a morass of information about the contents of his shopping trolley and the cats she thought she remembered homing with him years ago.

Poor Roger observed jokingly that it was to be hoped he wasn't an ex-inmate she'd met during her volunteering activities at the local prison as she could well have asked him a tactless question about holidays. Poor Roger then risked life and limb by sniggering at his little witticism. A loud crash followed as a jar of instant gravy granules slipped from the Earth Mother's grasp.

'D Wing!' she gasped weakly, 'it was D Wing. Well, how was I to know he'd turn up in Waitrose? Sneaking about by the frozen peas! I'd never have clapped eyes on him if you hadn't sent me off on a wild goose chase looking for BOGOF faggots!'

Poor Roger shrugged and wandered off to fill the bird feeders, beating off pigeons the size of helicopters as he clung to the stepladder with his free hand. Minutes later he returned, nursing a semi-severed digit and cursing the dear little squirrels for ripping open the latest rodent-proof bird feeder. The Earth Mother was unimpressed as he crossed the room in a manner reminiscent of Richard III.

'Why are you limping when you've cut your finger?' she enquired absent-mindedly. 'Thank goodness the squirrels didn't hurt themselves on that horrible plastic! I don't know why you didn't buy a better quality one!'

Poor Roger turned to me and smiled weakly. 'Have you noticed, Stumpy, old man, how everything's always our fault?'

'What rubbish!' trilled the Earth Mother. 'Only the other day I said it was my fault when I reversed into that man in the car park – even though he obviously shouldn't have been there and was totally to blame.'

I'd realised at an early stage that keeping in with Miss Elizabeth, our self-appointed head monitor, was essential to my survival in the twilight zone that was Tresta Towers and had discovered by sheer chance how to bring a smile to that pinched little face.

I think it's known as a "distressed" look in the coffee table glossies, but the furnishings at Tresta Towers had carried this to extremes. One particularly attractive feature was the woodchip wallpaper which adhered to the wall in dangling strips where it felt like it and for the most part didn't bother at all. Every now and then the breeze from the open patio door would set ribbons of paper fluttering in the most tempting manner, making it impossible for me not to pounce on them and pull them off the wall in lovely curly scrolls. Now old Lizzie just couldn't resist these wispy wonders and would play with them for hours. It was a small price to pay for keeping in with the old bitch.

Around this time a most unfortunate incident occurred rendering me mewless with pain. I'd been out in the garden all day and was just thinking I might give myself a treat by going in without indulging the humans in the usual hide-and-seek game which they enjoyed so much, when a kamikaze pine cone hurtled down and rapped me smartly on my poor little back leg.

It wasn't so bad at first, but by the time I'd rested up my leg was throbbing like Steve McQueen's motorbike. I clambered out of my igloo and limped across the room, making sure I chose the route between the humans and the telly. Just my luck – it was *The Great British Bake-Off* – nail-biting stuff which had the Earth Mother and Poor Roger remaining conscious for whole minutes at a time. The first limp-past went unnoticed, so I had to drag my poor broken body past again, then instantly wished I hadn't.

'Oh no – Stumpy's broken his leg! Roger – do something! Put the big light on!'

Poor Roger started flinging himself about, falling over Benjamin, the Earth Mother and half-a-dozen take-away containers, while I waited for the Earth Mother to make her "hot water and towels" speech.

Being totally freaked out by their behaviour, I thought the safest thing would be to limp back into my igloo, which I now realised I should never have left. I had so nearly made it when the Earth Mother grabbed me, causing me to scream and bite her arm. She put me down quite gently considering the loss of blood and staggered back to the sofa to lick her wounds – metaphorically speaking, of course. By the time that Mary Berry had sampled rather more than she needed to of the various signature bakes, the Earth Mother was on her hands and knees advancing towards my refuge. She cunningly held my head back with one hand while running the other down my poor injured leg.

'It's not broken!' she announced to the comatose forms on the sofa. 'I think he's making rather a lot of fuss about nothing. It's probably bruised, that's all.'

The next morning, she had me in that old cat carrier before the sun had ventured over the rather pretentious conservatory opposite. Off we thundered to the vet's where the over-enthusiastic locum manipulated my leg, shoved a needle in my neck and a worm pill down my throat without drawing breath. The connection between worms and my injured leg wasn't immediately apparent, but I suppose that's why vets have all those years of training.

For a moment I thought we might get back to the car park without the Earth Mother encountering anybody she knew, but this was obviously a ridiculous idea. A dishevelled and desperate-looking woman lugging an enormous cat-carrier was lurching towards the surgery. Looking similarly dishevelled and desperate was a large black and white cat with its grumpy face pressed against the bars.

The Earth Mother stopped abruptly, causing me to slither into the bars of my carrier.

'I must ask,' she simpered, 'did you get your cat from Woking Cats Protection?'

Instead of running in the opposite direction, possibly because of the weight she was carrying, the woman replied that indeed she had. She had adopted him from "some woman" living in a bungalow backing on to woods. This woman had lots of weird cats of her own and was "quite odd".

Some people would have left it at that, but not the Earth Mother.

'That was me!' she squeaked, taking the description as a compliment. 'I knew he was one of my babies! How long have you had Binky now?'

The poor woman was understandably shaken. 'I've had him for ten years,' she said. 'Fancy you remembering him after all that time!'

I wasn't surprised at all. The Earth Mother is extremely vague about most things, but can recognise one of her "babies" on a dark night, half-a-mile away. How useful this is when measured against remembering to buy milk and bread, or serve up meals before midnight, I'm not at all sure, but it has the advantage of frightening people on a fairly regular basis.

On the way back from the vet's, the tin box started to play up and I quite thought we would grind to a halt long before the familiar, and profoundly boring, outlines of Tresta Towers loomed into view. Luckily, we managed to coast into the drive before the engine finally spluttered into silence.

'Roger! Roger! There's something wrong with the car. The worming light came on, but I've no idea why.'

Poor Roger rushed in from restocking the bird feeders. He might just as well have given the cordon bleu fat balls straight to Mr Ratty-Chops, but that would have removed a valuable opportunity to commune with nature – or escape from a domestic crisis.

'What are you talking about? Worming light?'

The Earth Mother giggled irritatingly. 'Silly me! I meant warning light! It's Stumpy's fault. I asked the vet to worm him while we were there.'

I quite enjoyed being fussed over for a few hours, but within a very short time my leg had fully recovered and all I wanted to do was get out there and give those squirrels a bit of a shake up. The Earth Mother was no fun and insisted on keeping me banged up for a couple of days, until an all-out attack on the wallpaper had her pleading with me to go into the garden.

By then we were limbering up for Halloween and the Earth Mother was excitedly planning what to do with a pumpkin that she'd been given – presumably by someone who disliked her intensely. There seemed very little to recommend the ugly looking thing, which bore a striking resemblance to Benjamin Wobble with the light behind him. After several attempts to carve a face on it – on the pumpkin, I mean, not Benjamin Wobble – the Earth Mother consigned the wretched thing to the "conservation area", where it grinned lopsidedly at the pointy-faced badgers until the combined efforts of a particularly harsh winter and repeated spraying by a marauding tom cat eventually wiped the smile off its ghastly orange chops.

Around this time I heard a lot about things that go bump in the night, but failed to see the significance of this as hardly a week went by without more bumps in the night than most people have had hot dinners. Apart from the rather obvious "bump" of Evie leaping down from the top window in the bedroom, there were numerous other nocturnal disturbances. Poor Roger's fitful snoring took a bit of getting used to, but personally I found the Earth Mother's wheezing and snuffling much harder to cope with. I kept thinking old Brillo Badger had taken up residence – a suspicion which was almost impossible to dislodge after I accidentally glimpsed the Earth Mother in her new and ultra glamorous black and white winceyette nightdress.

Great Uncle Tigger's constipation was a constant worry and played a larger part in the Earth Mother's life than might be considered natural in normal households. Usually, regular administration of some ghastly brown goo would sort things out, but sometimes the Earth Mother would retire to bed with Great Uncle's predicament uppermost in her mind. She would typically have spent the previous hour or so trailing round after the old wreck while he clambered on and off every dirt tray in the place with disappointment at every turn. Consequently, a satisfying "plop" from some distant corner of the bungalow would bring relief – not just to Great Uncle, but to the Earth Mother, who would call out, 'Well done, Great Uncle!' and subside into happy snuffling within moments.

Another source of nocturnal spookiness concerned unexplained noises, usually of a retching-type nature. The Earth Mother was famous for having slept through the Great Hurricane of 1987, when a ninety-foot tree crashed down yards from Tresta Towers, but the sound of a cat chucking up would have her wide awake and out of bed in seconds. She would blunder from room to room to find us all in our beds, sleeping the sleep of the innocent, and return to bed with frozen feet and a conspicuous lack of goodwill.

Occasionally, the phantom fur ball would turn up weeks later, silhouetted against the shredded wallpaper on the back of a chair, or adhering to a table leg in defiance of the laws of gravity. The Earth Mother would whoop with delight at the resolution of one of life's teasing little mysteries and drag Poor Roger along to witness the unlikely cause of her jubilation.

Magazines and junk mail cascading down from the

dining room table were a fairly routine occurrence when St Petersburg Cloud Princess left her igloo for a stroll round the decks. She would stretch out her knobbly little legs and the latest Argos catalogue would plummet, frequently followed by Princess, who would glare at the offending publication and wash her bottom – if she could locate it under the candyfloss.

I soon realised that there was no time of day or night when one could comfortably look forward to being bored. The other morning I'd no sooner hauled myself into my little coracle bed on the sofa when I became aware of frantic scrabbling sounds emanating from the waste paper bin. Peering blearily over the rim of my bed, I saw that Benjamin Wobble had "fellded" in because a thoughtless visitor had assumed that the weighty catalogue across the top of the bin had arrived there by accident whereas it was in fact a stepping stone for Benjy to access the heady heights of the sofa. I popped down to have a better look. Viewed from ground level, Benjy looked like a particularly floppy glove puppet, but considerably less animated.

By the time the Earth Mother had blundered into the lounge, poor old Benjamin was becoming hysterical in an understated way. That is to say, his front paws were gradually losing their grip and his mouth was opening and shutting soundlessly as he slipped further into the abyss – saved from hitting rock bottom by a sea of Crunchie wrappers and empty Malteser packets.

'Stumpy! Did you push poor Benjy in there?' she demanded.

Yeah – like I got hold of the book and carried it across to the coffee table; stupid woman!

'Benjy! Mummy's here! Where's my brave little soldier?'

It took several attempts to pull the ginger lump out, during the course of which he "talked" incessantly and dribbled copiously over the Earth Mother and over himself, so that by the time they came up for air they both looked as if they'd swum the Channel on a particularly stormy day. Our hero had to be rewarded for his courage in the face of a seriously threatening waste paper bin and was comforted with half a chicken and a whole Webbox stick. This stiffened the wobbly one's resolve to the point where he felt brave enough to mountaineer back up the north face of the bin and repeat the performance.

'Brave little Benjy-Boo!' cooed the Earth Mother, 'it's just like when I fell off that donkey at Margate as a child. I knew the only thing to do was to get straight back on.'

CHAPTER EIGHT

Puzzles and Predicaments

Unsurprisingly, as Poor Roger ventured further into the challenging world of wildlife photography, he found he needed more and more equipment. What he saved on travel to foreign parts – there being any number of models vying for his attention in the back garden – Poor Roger spent on photographic accessories. Having acquired an enviable array of lenses and tripods – and I'm not including Whizzy – he quite naturally needed a suitable rucksack to carry everything in. Great was his excitement when a large parcel arrived. This happy development coincided with the Earth Mother's decision to inflict herself on one of her cronies for coffee and the endless putting-the-world-to-rights stuff that was such a feature of their get-togethers.

The least we could do was enter into the spirit of things and in no time at all Evie, Lucio and little old me had ripped the paper to shreds, jumped on dangling straps and investigated numerous compartments. The pensioners dribbled away on the sofa oblivious to the excitement of it all and Poor Roger desperately struggled to interest us in going outside. Not a hope! Not while there was rustling paper to hide in and straps to kill!

Eventually he succeeded in hoisting the rucksack up on his back, strutting round the bungalow like a Velcro-encrusted beetle.

'This is going to be so useful, Benjy-Boo!' he gushed. 'Just wait till the chaps at the Photographic Society clock this!'

Benjamin Wobble might have shared Poor Roger's excitement, but he gave every appearance of being fast asleep – probably because he had deduced that the cause of the fuss was inedible unless you happened to be an exceptionally hungry goat. After walking round for some time, Poor Roger thought he would abandon the beetle impersonation and attempted to shrug off the weighty carapace. Ten minutes later, he was still shrugging and becoming dangerously mottled in the face.

'How much longer is that woman going to be?' he muttered, rubbing himself against the door jamb in a desperate attempt to free himself. 'Where did she say she was going? On an expedition to the bloody North Pole?!'

While Poor Roger grew increasingly hot and breathless, the Earth Mother – having enjoyed more cups of coffee than Starbucks usually serve in a week – had progressed to the supermarket where she promptly met most of the people she's ever passed the time of day with. By the time she wandered back to Tresta Towers, Poor Roger had managed to rid himself of the troublesome rucksack and was sweating shakily on the sofa between Bonnie Bun-Bun and Miss Elizabeth.

'Did you get those shrubs planted?' trilled the Earth Mother, picking her way past a heap of shredded packing and the jettisoned rucksack. 'I hope you remembered to dig in plenty of compost!'

Never one to notice the odd menacing silence, the Earth Mother held aloft the source of Poor Roger's chagrin.

'Well – this looks rather jolly! Have you tried it on yet?'

Loyalty prevents me from providing a detailed account of the conversation that followed, but suffice it to say that lunch was considerably later than usual and the rucksack found itself banished to the naughty cupboard for some time to come.

Around the same time, the Earth Mother decided to throw a cup of coffee over the keyboard of the laptop and was amazed when it slowed to a relentless and glutinous halt. Presenting the offending article to an unsuspecting expert, the Earth Mother giggled when he removed the keyboard to expose not just congealing coffee, but a significant amount of cat fur.

'It would be strange if there wasn't!' she sniggered, 'because Evie's just finished typing her manuscript and Stumpy Malone's well on the way with his!'

'Of course,' said the man, smiling nervously. 'The new keyboard should be here in a couple of days or so. Do tell Stumpy Malone he'll have his laptop back soon!'

The laptop returned in the twinkling of an eye to everybody's relief, particularly Poor Roger's, as the Earth Mother had felt the need to check her emails on the hour, every hour, on his computer. After many a merry chortle, she would then reply at length to the numerous challenged correspondents who sought her views about essential cat matters, such as the consistency of Snowflake's latest poo, or the need to control Kevin the kitten's kamikaze exploits in the conservatory.

This meant that Poor Roger, returning home from a wild and windy photographic shoot behind the summerhouse, would have to wait until the Earth Mother vacated the seat of power before he could peruse his winning shots on the screen. Not only did she sit there bashing away for hours, but having eventually staggered off to grab a handful of coffee granules, she would criticise the speed and efficiency of the long-suffering machine.

'Clunky old keyboard!' she would chirrup, disappearing into the depths of the wine cupboard. 'You'd find it really annoying if you spent more time on it.'

Cloud Princess's knickers were a perpetual source of worry as the old tart spent so many hours dribbling into her candyfloss-clad hindquarters that a certain amount of clumping was inevitable. Mr Comby could only achieve so much and every now and then a more radical makeover was called for. This necessitated making a double length appointment at the vet's and it took all the Earth Mother's resilience to break through the barricades. As soon as she realised who was on the phone, the vet would signal frantically from the doorway in a desperate effort to convey to the receptionist that she was about to depart on a three year sabbatical to Tibet to study genital abnormalities in yaks. Unfortunately for the vet, the Earth Mother would persist until she succeeded in pinning down a new and untested member of staff, who would innocently make the booking and then wonder why she was consigned to feral cat handling for six months.

On this particular occasion, we waved the happy couple off and slunk back to bed, confident that our gain was the vet's loss. Much innocent amusement was to be had when the Earth Mother returned, clutching a reclusive and embarrassed Persian concealed under a shredded blanket.

'We're back!' yodelled the Earth Mother – quite unnecessarily as the crashing of the cat carrier against the door, the walls and Benjamin's furry little head resembled the racket caused by one of the badgers' more violent attacks on the patio pots.

With a flourish, the Earth Mother opened the carrier and whipped off the remains of the top blanket to reveal what appeared to be a cross between a Mexican hairless dog and a lump of candyfloss. It was hard to tell if dear Bella was in a mood as that "walked into a wall" face didn't really do smiling, but I would have been ready to kill.

'Doesn't she look lovely?' cooed our heroine. 'And the vet was so kind, – she didn't charge us anything!'

I can only assume that the woman was lightheaded with relief at completing this nightmare assignment and only just restrained herself from giving the Earth Mother money to leave and never return.

Poor Roger rallied quickly, joining in the prevailing mood of elation when it was quite clear to the rest of us that the vet owed Cloud Princess an apology if not several thousands of pounds in compensation. I did tell the Persian about those firms that specialise in getting you a fortune in damages for even quite minor mishaps, but by then she'd retreated into the depths of her igloo. That cat could have been looking at a pretty hefty old payout if she'd played her cards right.

The very next morning I noticed that Poor Roger was regarding the Earth Mother's open diary with rather more attention than usual. As the Earth Mother breezed into the study and slumped in front of the computer, he brandished the offending volume.

'I see you're meeting "K" again. And the day after tomorrow as well!'

The Earth Mother simpered. 'What are you talking

about, dear? I'm in all day today. I've got the housework to do. It's "K" for Katalax. You know Great Uncle's bowels need a bit of encouragement and a good squeeze every other day seems to do the trick.'

Great Uncle Tigger's ragged old ears twitched as the last few words sank in. I had presumed she was referring to squeezing the Katalax tube, but the alarm on the ancient one's face made me reconsider.

'Well, that's a disappointment,' mumbled Poor Roger. 'I was hoping "K" might have been a dab hand with a duster. When Evie trotted across my desk this morning, I nearly choked to death!'

The Earth Mother assumed a wounded expression. 'I always enjoy dusting, as you well know, but when I did it a couple of months ago it made Isabelle sneeze.'

Poor Roger obviously lacked the strength to question this assertion and returned to the computer to browse through a thousand badger pictures. Just before midnight he'd managed to sneak up on old Brillo tucking into his usual sumptuous supper on a slab by the summerhouse and rattled off a few shots. Such was Poor Roger's enthusiasm that he edged nearer and nearer to the smelly old thing to the point where Brillo thought his Chinese takeaway was under threat and made his feelings clear in the form of a deeply unattractive, yellow-toothed snarl.

'Oh, bless him! Old Brillo's smiling!' exclaimed the Earth Mother rapturously as we viewed this frightening spectacle, 'couldn't you just cuddle him to bits!'

Count Lucio, who was reclining on the desk, yawned and stared at her in amazement. One thing badgers are not is cuddly and even Lucio – not the sharpest tool in the box – had always given them a wide berth. Poking the old dog fox in the chops was one thing, but messing with the worm-raker was quite another.

Meanwhile, my own hunting skills were coming along in leaps and bounds and I'd actually got my front paws on that extremely irritating squirrel more than once, only to feel its slippery little body wriggle free. It was in situations like this that I regretted my lack of hind paws. Even one hind paw would have given me a bit more pouncing ability, as demonstrated by three-legged Whizzy, who could achieve major lift-off with one push of that formidable hind foot.

I was making good headway with the mice and Evie came close to smiling upon me, taking full credit for my success as usual. I thought it would be good to attempt a bit of laddish bonding with Benjamin Wobble, but ungrateful didn't come close. As soon as I approached with a vole dangling moustache-like from my jaws, old Wobble disappeared behind the sofa and didn't reappear for hours.

I had assumed that when the Earth Mother sat at the computer, she might actually be doing something important and it took me some time to realise that much of the time was frittered away "surfing the net". One dramatic find was a video of a cat with artificial back feet. This unfortunate creature had suffered a traumatic accident which resulted in the loss of both paws and the lower part of his legs, but was now bounding around on his artificial pins.

'Just like those athletes in the Olympics!' mused our heroine. 'I wonder if that could work for Stumpy?'

I had a sudden vision of myself in Lycra, draped in a Union Jack, flaunting my gold medal and springing round the stadium to rapturous applause. I would make moving speeches, thanking Evie and Lucio for their unfailing support and the cat food giants would vie with each other to gain my paw of approval. Just as I was warming to the idea of a glittering future, the Earth Mother's shrill tones brought me back to the Land of a Thousand Dirt Trays with an extremely unpleasant bump.

'Good Lord! £15,000 smackers! Well, you've had that, Stumpy Malone. And anyway, I saw you sprinting across the garden after that pigeon, so I think you can manage quite nicely without any modifications.'

This was, of course, irritatingly true. The ends of my back legs had calloused over to form imitation paws and I really wasn't prevented from doing anything that a cat needs to do, apart from having a really good scratch behind each ear. Still, it wouldn't have hurt the Earth Mother to at least consider the possibilities for more than a second before she dived back into the delights of the thermal underwear website.

The dowager duchesses, Miss Elizabeth and Miss Isabelle, were just saying how pleasurable the recent weekends had been with the Earth Mother and Poor Roger out visiting various unfortunate friends and relatives when the Earth Mother came crashing back from the supermarket with three tons of food. One look at that intense mottled face was enough to persuade most of us that leaving the kitchen as rapidly as possible was a pretty good idea. Most of us, but not Count Lucio, who made a grave error of judgement in thinking his Italian charm would more than compensate for knocking a carton of Mr Waitrose's ready-made custard across the floor. As the bright yellow lake spread slowly and relentlessly under the cooker, a large and exceedingly foolish black cat made the best decision of his adult life and accelerated past me to take refuge in the woods.

It was a Sunday morning and our domestic goddess was in the kitchen, preparing a delicious meal for our unsuspecting guests. At precisely one minute past eleven, Great Uncle Tigger began to shuffle from dirt tray to dirt tray. I'm sure it was pure coincidence that the vet's surgery closed at eleven, but it was certainly an unfortunate one. Eventually – somewhere between shoving a lump of meat in the oven and shredding her fingers along with the parsnips – the Earth Mother noticed Great Uncle's pained expression and muffled grunts.

She promptly abandoned the lunch and trailed round after our hero, who threatened to arrive in Melbourne any minute if the frantic digging was anything to go by. At least Tigger could rely on Benjamin Wobble's support in his hour of need – if a good bonk from a furry pumpkin could be considered helpful.

'Roger! Where are you?' she shrieked. 'Poor Uncle Tigger's got naughty bottom problems!'

Instinctively, Poor Roger headed for the garden, but the Earth Mother was too quick for him.

'You'll have to go to the chemist and get those things – you know – enema things! And chuck the potatoes in the oven on your way out!'

Poor Roger roared off, no doubt realising that driving round Woking on what could well be a hopeless quest was preferable to being anywhere near Great Uncle's bottom.

He returned, triumphantly clutching a box of ghastly looking plastic tubes which were, apparently, about to transform Great Uncle's life.

'Hold him! Hold him – I can't get it in with him wriggling about like that!' Poor Roger had Tigger pinned to the doormat while the Earth Mother rummaged about under his tail.

'There we are – that should do it! It says they take between five and fifteen minutes to work, so you keep an eye on him and I'll get on with the lunch. They'll be here in a minute!'

By the time our guests arrived, a few sad little dollops were all that Great Uncle had managed, but exhaustion had set in and he was fast asleep in his bed. The Earth Mother inevitably felt the need to inform the gathering of the morning's trials and tribulations, the result being that only the bravest and least imaginative elected to sample the chocolate pudding.

After a peaceful but unproductive night, our little hero was whisked off to the vet's, to return a thinner and considerably more cheerful cat, even if his ginger trousers were a bit suspect in the personal freshness department. Whizzy took one sniff and flung herself at the door, but the rest of us decided to suffer in silence as Bonnie Bun-Bun reported seeing a large chicken being thrust into the oven.

Over the next few days, Tigger's successes on the dirt tray were greeted with wild jubilation, which probably said more than anybody ever wanted to know about life at Tresta Towers.

CHAPTER NINE

The Dinosaur Zone

Being a kitten of the electronic age, I became painfully aware of the Earth Mother's failure to grasp the rudiments of technology at an early stage. Her standard response to most problems involving inanimate things was to thump the offending item and threaten it with a one-way trip to the rubbish tip. Every now and then this worked – particularly with the ancient Honda car which had shared so many of her adventures over the years. This solid and uncomplaining vehicle had transported more unneutered feral tomcats than anyone with a sense of smell would ever want to contemplate and survived off-road experiences which would have had any self-respecting Land Rover longing for the reassuring boredom of Woking High Street.

Most of these reckless enterprises had involved the trapping of feral cats and the innocent volunteers that the Earth Mother tricked into accompanying her would return hours later, pale and shaken and smelling strongly of many odours – none of them pleasant. Occasionally the car would "play up" and feign illness, but was no match for the Earth Mother in one of her determined moods and a swift kick in the tyres would usually bring it to its senses.

This robust approach to rectifying faults was less effective with the more sensitive appliances such as telephones and computers. Whereas Poor Roger would relish the challenge, the Earth Mother took the slightest malfunction as a personal slight. When the telephone became terminally ill, however, even Poor Roger's expertise couldn't revive it.

'I think Miss Elizabeth knows more about this than she's letting on!' snapped the Earth Mother. 'I'm sure I put the cover back over the phone when I went to bed last night, but it was on the floor this morning and there was a distinct whiff of cat pee.'

I could have said so much. It was in the early hours that Miss Elizabeth – no doubt avenging herself for an ill-judged reprimand some days previously – clambered on to the sideboard, whisked the blue plastic box off the phone with one expert paw flick and sprayed copiously over the unsuspecting handset. To anybody who suffers under the delusion that girl cats can't spray, I can only suggest that they visit Tresta Towers on a bad day. Actually, we rarely have any other sort, but some are just awful in an average sort of way, whereas others achieve a level of dreadfulness that would make eating slugs seem an attractive alternative.

In an effort to cope with Miss Elizabeth's "challenging" behaviour, the Earth Mother had draped a selection of gaudily striped and absorbent towels over various items of furniture. I'm sure the glossier magazines would have killed to feature her idiosyncratic approach to interior design, but reporters may have been dissuaded from conducting an in-depth interview after clocking Miss Elizabeth's menacing smile through the dining room window.

Anyway, after much mopping and lamentation, the Earth Mother and Poor Roger finally accepted that the phone had died and set off, clutching the blue plastic box, to obtain a replacement. Although it had failed to measure up in this instance, this ice cream box had done noble work over the years in protecting various telephones from Miss Elizabeth's thoughtless behaviour.

I tried not to think of the bemused, spiky-haired youth who would have been pinned against the wall and interrogated about a suitable replacement.

'We've got telephones with integral answerphones, telephones with full internet functionality, automatic selective redial options, remote access duality... Tell me what's important to you and I'll tell you what you need to purchase.'

At this point, no doubt, the Earth Mother would have brandished the blue ice cream box and explained that the one essential feature was that the new phone would fit inside the box because Miss Elizabeth was inclined to pee on the phone if anything had upset her.

'She's a lovely cat,' the Earth Mother would have said with touching loyalty, 'but she does take things to heart. Still, I'm sure you've felt like that yourself sometimes.'

Miss Elizabeth also showed a lively interest in the laptop and enjoyed nothing more than a quick frolic across the keyboard when the Earth Mother was framing one of her more intense and anguished poems. These unique works were usually destined for the latest competition in a literary magazine she had recently subscribed to, and which had a mercifully small circulation.

Sometimes, the Earth Mother – drained no doubt by the emotional demands of the latest composition – would fail to notice Miss Elizabeth's winning touches and send the manuscript off into the ether, liberally spattered with asterisks and exclamation marks.

The real dramas occurred when Miss Elizabeth was in one of her "delete and be damned" moods. She would bide her time until the Earth Mother had abandoned the computer to seek sustenance, then hurl her diminutive white and tabby body across the keyboard, dancing up and down until various messages had flashed up all over the screen warning of the most dire consequences – famine and pestilence being hardly worth mentioning by comparison. By the time the Earth Mother had struggled back, there would be no sign of her latest masterpiece and every sign of Miss Elizabeth, nonchalantly picking her feet on the corner of the desk.

Sometimes, when pushed for time, Elizabeth would content herself with firing off an email that even the Earth Mother would have refrained from sending given the chance to reflect for one or two seconds. A notable triumph was telling the council's planning officer exactly what she thought he should do following the approval of plans for an industrial unit the size of an aircraft hanger to be built down the road. The Earth Mother was particularly grieved that she hadn't had the chance to check it through, but whether or not she would have amended the spelling of "bustard" remains a matter for conjecture.

When one of the Earth Mother's cronies came round recently, I was fascinated to learn that her cat has his own Facebook page. Not only does Daisy have his own page – yes, there was a gender identification issue when he was a kitten – but he has an international network of cat friends. These friends send photographs and exchange information about the latest cat toys; they also offer emotional support to each other in times of stress, which means they're kept pretty damn busy.

I was quick to see the attractions of social networking and foolishly mentioned this to Great Uncle Tigger, who looked at me as if I'd said I could see the attractions of dogs.

'No good will come of it!' he asserted with unaccustomed vigour. 'Mark my words, young Stumpy, there are things out there in space that are best left undisturbed. If you start sending messages into the ether, the howling monsters will know where to find you and you'll be snatched from your bed!'

I was puzzled at first, but soon remembered that poor old Tigger had been snatched from his bed that very morning to be dosed up with laxatives by the Earth Mother, one of the most terrifying howling monsters you'd never wish to meet.

This dire warning failed to deter me from getting my cute little paws on the keyboard whenever the Earth Mother left it unattended and I struck up a particularly rewarding correspondence with a rather knowing little tortoiseshell number, Miss Pickle of Apethorpe Spa. This little minx, who lived with an undemanding and unimaginative companion named Spooks, took a harsh view of her human servant, who apparently toiled night and day to provide a veritable running buffet of yummy meals.

Benjamin Wobble also took to the keyboard, corresponding with a dog called Toffee, who was ginger like him and had a boyfriend who tended to pee on her. Old Porky was fascinated by this unusual love token and might have been encouraged to try it out on Miss

Elizabeth, had his wobbliness not prevented the realisation of this particularly dubious ambition.

One object which resolutely refused to be intimidated by the Earth Mother's outbursts – apart from Miss Elizabeth – was the trusty vacuum cleaner. This venerable machine was called "Henry" and had survived for years with a rather unsettling smile on its face – a smile which had remained intact regardless of crunching collisions with doors, skirting boards and the Earth Mother's legs.

I soon realised that Henry wasn't just a smiley face. His cheery demeanour concealed a malevolent tendency to consume cat toys, mouse remains and a range of vital objects such as small keys, necessitating a messy and often unproductive search through the unsavoury contents of his dust bag.

Most of us regarded Henry's occasional trundles as no more than fleeting inconveniences, but to Benjamin Wobble they were the equivalent of a waking nightmare in which his flabby little body would be sucked up by the smiley monster at any moment. Because of this attention-seeking behaviour, the vacuum cleaning had to happen on a dry day so that Poor Roger could take Benjamin into the garden away from all that dreadful commotion; the vacuum cleaner made a lot of noise too.

'Roger,' the Earth Mother would call, 'do you think it's going to keep dry? I need to get Henry out, but I don't want Benjamin to be fritted!'

I'm absolutely certain that expeditions have departed for Antarctica with less fuss. Having consulted and debated the weather forecast, Poor Roger would endeavour to rouse Benjamin and lure him into the garden by trailing various exciting toys past his snotty little nose. Once he'd admitted defeat, Poor Roger would hoist old Porky off the sofa and cart him off to the wilds of the conservation area, while Henry snuffled up toys and valuables with joyful abandon. He made very little impression on dirt and dust, so I presume this wasn't in his job description.

After a few minutes, Poor Roger and Benjamin would appear at the patio door, each as desperate as the other.

'Haven't you finished yet? Benjamin's getting very upset and I think he might have a fit.'

At the mention of the "fit" word, the Earth Mother dragged Henry into the mysterious recess where he slumbered in between outings and rushed back to distract Benjy with a Webbox stick.

As Miss Isabelle often remarked, Benjamin's behaviour could be a real pain in the bottom and frequently delayed important things like the preparation of supper. The worst thing about old Porky's "turns" was the unpredictability. There were some things that you could rely on. Tall people standing in a doorway with the light behind them always sent poor Benjy into a fit, so that anyone guilty of this inconsiderate behaviour risked being dragged into the room by the Earth Mother or Poor Roger and pushed down on the nearest sofa. Plastic bags also had a lot to answer for, particularly if they made a noise just as our hero was wobbling past.

The burglar alarm, which made the most awful noise when the humans returned from their various excitements, failed to make any impact on Benjamin; he was also unimpressed by the badgers wiping their slobbery snouts over the patio door, but the mere sight of a Chihuahua could send him into orbit.

Anyway, the upshot of all this was that the vacuuming

rarely assumed priority at Tresta Towers, leaving the Earth Mother plenty of time to concentrate on other domestic pursuits, including gossiping and consuming large quantities of El Plonko.

For many years, the installation of a burglar alarm had been the subject of lively debate at Tresta Towers. Poor Roger argued the case rationally and eloquently and the Earth Mother threw unreasonable tantrums and sulked for days whenever the subject was mentioned. No prizes for guessing which approach carried the day.

The turning point was a throwaway remark made by Poor Roger after the latest mindless break-in a few streets away.

'It's not what they take,' he observed, 'it's the damage and upset. You imagine if they kicked the door in and all the cats wandered off into the night... '

The Earth Mother looked up from poking the cabbage and stared at him.

'But we haven't got anything worth taking!' she whined. 'Surely they wouldn't try and break in here?'

It may be that Poor Roger sensed a weakness in his opponent, or he may simply have been voicing his fears, but his next utterance was the clincher.

'Of course, the worst thing of all would be if they hurt the cats or kidnapped them... '

The Earth Mother clutched at her throat; her lips moved soundlessly as she snatched me up and hugged me to her cabbage-scented jumper.

Within weeks an alarm had been installed and Poor Roger tried hard to conceal his delight at achieving the installation of yet another device about which the Earth Mother would not have a clue. A series of training sessions followed which had to be aborted after about ten seconds as the Earth Mother was invariably distracted by the need to check whether Great Uncle's laxative had worked yet. Eventually she reached a level of proficiency in burglar alarm setting that a reasonably bright sea slug might have aspired to in half the time.

It took considerably longer for her to become fond of the system, but in due course she warmed to the comforting glow of its lights in the hours of darkness and even entered into the nocturnal excitements that could be enjoyed by waving her arms about while lying in bed. Next time you're wondering what to worry about, spare a thought for me as I toss about on their bed while the Earth Mother and Poor Roger roll around, waving at the sensor in the corner of the room.

'Ooh,' shrieks the Earth Mother, 'it's gone red! Look – I've made it go red. It only went green when you waved at it!'

Or you might prefer to think about the hapless burglar who in a rash moment might choose to break into Tresta Towers. Would it really be the burglar alarm that frightened him off or the sight of two blobby old pensioners rolling about in bed shrieking with laughter and waving at the wall?

It should have come as no surprise that when she heard that the spectacular show *Walking with Dinosaurs* was coming to London, the Earth Mother became obsessed with obtaining tickets, presumably in the hope of catching up with some technologically challenged Stegosaurus. Understandably filled with fear when he saw her podgy fingers hovering over the keyboard, Poor Roger took command of the situation and booked two tickets rather than have the Earth Mother inadvertently book the whole of the O2 stadium.

When the great day dawned, the mounting excitement communicated itself to the old fluffball, St Petersburg Cloud Princess, who was determined to stow away in the Earth Mother's rucksack along with any number of chocolate bars, claw clippers and worm pills – all "must haves" for a day trip to London.

The Earth Mother was entranced. 'Bella wants to meet the dinosaurs!' she trilled, extracting the squeaking lump of candyfloss for the umpteenth time. 'She knows the dinosaurs would love her, but the noise they make would be very frightening for a little pussycat!'

Never have I been more thankful to hear the door slam. Did she realise the "dinosaurs" were actually made of foam and rubber with men inside them? As Miss Elizabeth so often observed, it might seem like a good idea to ask the question, but it certainly wasn't worth waiting for the answer.

CHAPTER TEN

Enthusiasms

I still tremble to think about the day I inadvertently glanced at the Earth Mother's diary and saw that she was due to perform a parachute jump that very afternoon. The thought of that fat, flailing body plummeting from the sky was the stuff of nightmares and I feared for any wildlife that might inadvertently flap or stumble into her flight path.

Miss Elizabeth yawned in an exaggerated manner and spent at least five minutes washing her whiskers before she deigned to put my mind at rest.

'That's nothing!' she snorted, 'didn't you notice that she was making an attempt on the land speed record the other morning – in the car park outside Sainsbury's?'

'In the ancient Honda Civic?' I squealed. 'It's always touch and go whether the old wreck will make it to the corner of the road – and the car's a bit dodgy too!'

Miss Elizabeth looked at me pityingly and explained that one of the Earth Mother's cronies had recently suggested that she should try to broaden her horizons.

'It's all very well knowing a lot about worming treatments and flea stuff, but there is a whole world out there if you took the trouble to look. You could learn another language or study something different. We all need to venture beyond our comfort zone!' she had said encouragingly.

The Earth Mother seized upon this well-intentioned advice and responded with spirit.

'I'm getting really good at understanding what Benjy says and I don't just know about fleas and worms,' she said in a slightly hurt tone, 'I'm pretty good at claw-clipping – and I know a lot about cat-friendly stain removal products!'

One characteristic shared by the Earth Mother's friends is an abundance of stamina; after a mere three hours, this particular crony had succeeded in convincing the Earth Mother that she should branch out beyond her present wide-ranging activities to embrace some new interests. That is to say, she had convinced the Earth Mother that it would be a jolly thing to record some exciting things in her diary, which in the Earth Mother's mind was as good as doing them.

Needless to say, I was greatly relieved by this explanation as supper was often late without the additional impediment of the old girl breaking every bone in her body if she happened to land on a spiky pine tree or a pottering badger.

Even though this nightmare had receded, there was still plenty to worry about. One day, for example, a poster arrived of a Scottish wildcat called "Sid". The Earth Mother was thrilled and in no time at all Sid was leering down at us in what I can only describe as a less than friendly manner.

'Isn't he handsome?' cooed the Earth Mother. 'I'd love to run my fingers through that wonderful tabby fur!'

Miss Elizabeth commented drily that should this wish be granted, the Earth Mother's days of applying flea treatments and shoving pills down reluctant furry throats could well be at an end. Indeed, far from being a cuddly sort of cat, old Sid looked like a diminutive and particularly bad-tempered tiger. Miss Isabelle thought he looked rather attractive, but judgement has never been her strongest attribute as we'd observed when she developed an ill-advised passion for the rabid rottweiler down the road.

Predictably, Benjamin Wobble thought that a good bonk would cheer Sid up, but one glance at those flattened ears and snarling jowls made this seem about as likely as a boa constrictor winning a boxing match.

Meanwhile, the rest of us experienced a growing uneasiness about the reason for Sid's appearance on the wall, not helped by the Earth Mother's tendency to talk to him every time she wafted past.

'Well, Sid,' she would chirrup, 'what do you think I should do about Bun-Bun's teeth?'

Not only would she talk to him, she would also – worryingly – regale us with Sid's answers.

'I think Sid's right,' she would observe. 'Bun-Bun's teeth are dreadful, but it doesn't stop her eating and the anaesthetic might be too much for her at her age. I think we'll leave well alone.'

Bonnie Bun-Bun was quick to see the advantages of Sid's homespun wisdom, having never let her dodgy teeth get between her and a piece of chicken.

Poor Roger was also the lucky recipient of Sid's opinions on such diverse subjects as the lawn needing mowing and the wine stocks running low.

'Yes – you're absolutely right, Sid! That grass has got *very* long. And the wine! I'm sure there were more bottles than that before the weekend.'

We had just started to get used to Sid snarling down at us when there was a further – and most alarming – development. The day had dawned innocently enough. Indeed, there had been considerable rejoicing over St Petersburg Cloud Princess piddling on the puppy pad with only minor leakage under the skirting board and by the time that Bun-Bun had swallowed her Felimazole tablet at the third attempt the mood was dangerously buoyant. In fact, the Earth Mother's mood was pretty buoyant all day; it was the rest of us that were reaching for the happy pills.

The Earth Mother scudded through life convinced that the next post would contain news of a distant and unbelievably rich relative who had popped his clogs and desired her to be the sole beneficiary of his estate. This meant that whenever the postman shoved half a ton of Damart and Cotton Traders catalogues through the door, she would swoop on them with the speed of a bulky sparrowhawk and spend the next hour grappling with the inevitable disappointment.

On this particular day, however, the catalogues were recycled almost before they landed and the Earth Mother retired to the sofa clutching a cold cup of coffee and a letter which was destined to fill us with dread.

'Roger! Roger! It's come. The adoption certificate for Sid! And there's all sorts of information about what he likes to eat!'

Even Benjamin Wobble stopped gathering up his bed in preparation for a pre-lunch bonk and gave the Earth Mother a vacant full frontal stare. Miss Elizabeth washed her whiskers so frantically that I thought she would never confidently negotiate a narrow space again and St

Petersburg Cloud Princess embarked on a stress-related sneezing spree that threatened to splatter not just the dining room table, but most of downtown Woking.

Count Lucio and Evie skipped into the garden and I scooted after them with as much speed as I could muster. The thought of Hissing Sid sprawled across the Earth Mother's lap while we were trying to concentrate on the complexities of an episode of Poirot that we'd only seen five times previously didn't bear thinking about. Evie swore – she did that a lot anyway – that she could feel Sid's hot breath on the back of her neck and Lucio said that he was only worried that he might hurt Sid if it came to a showdown. Yeah – like those flabby muscles would be a threat to a cat who looked like he'd breakfasted on six inch nails washed down with paint stripper!

We spent the next few days dreading the arrival of a reinforced crate containing the new arrival, but nothing more threatening than yet another delivery of must-have Damart underwear darkened the doorstep. Eventually, when a cuddly seal toy arrived on the scene, closely followed by a lopsided lion, I experienced one of those non-ecological light bulb moments. Even the Earth Mother couldn't seriously imagine that a blubbery old seal could be happy wallowing about in the sink-sized water feature down the garden. This was just another pathetic attempt on the Earth Mother's part to broaden her horizons by "adopting" various endangered animals across the globe. Predictably, Benjamin was disappointed as he had been looking forward to meeting his new friends, but the rest of us breathed a sigh of relief and waited for the next crisis.

Much more frightening for Poor Roger than the conservation phase was the Earth Mother's brief flirtation with domesticity. In no time at all she'd amassed a collection of hardware that wouldn't have looked out of place at Anne Boleyn's execution and was crashing about in the kitchen while arguing spiritedly with Count Lucio, who refused to budge from the work top, often looming darkly behind clouds of steam or helping himself to the odd lump of butter.

We would often see the fruits of her labours strewn across the badgers' supper venue, where sad failures would linger for several days before Poor Roger finally put an end to the Earth Mother's oft-rehearsed speeches on ingratitude.

'I just can't believe that those pointy-faced badgers would rather have worms than my lovely fruit tarts!' she would remark.

'It defies belief, dear!' Poor Roger would respond in his kindly way, hoping upon hope that she'd never find the grenade-like muffin he'd hidden in the cat poo bag.

Mercifully, this outbreak of culinary activity was short-lived and we all survived with more or less a full complement of limbs and digits – all except Whizzy and me, of course, but she'd lost her leg some years previously and I'd never had paws on my manly little hind legs.

The next enthusiasm involved terrorising small children and I was amazed that the authorities didn't take a stronger line from the start. I blamed the people at Cats Protection, naturally. Whatever did they think they were doing, unleashing the Earth Mother on whole classes of innocent boys and girls? What had they done to deserve such a punishment?

She would clatter off with a carload of "goody bags" and a sack containing such excitements as cat bowls and flea combs and return hours later, fit for nothing after separating two six-year old thugs who were knocking six bells out of each other and trying to silence Olivia, who knew more than anyone else wanted to hear about parasitic worms.

At one talk the Earth Mother had decided to discuss feline behaviour and interaction in rather more detail than usual. She had a collection of photographs, showing a lack-lustre assortment of felines in various random poses and the children were asked to identify why Fluffy had her ears back, or why Blackie might be arching his back.

After this illuminating session, one small child embarked on a longwinded account of two cats she'd been watching in her garden. The bigger ginger cat had jumped on the small white cat and grabbed it by the neck and Mummy had said they were fighting, but Chloe didn't find this convincing. The Earth Mother explained that the two cats were probably really good friends and were playing a game, to which Chloe replied that she didn't think the Earth Mother knew much about cats because her classmate Philip said the big cat was probably "giving her one". The Earth Mother thought this was highly amusing and almost regretted treading on Philip's foot as she left.

I was busy developing my own hobbies as I grew up and spent a lot of time trying to catch things to help Poor Roger with his photography. I wish I could adequately describe his expressions of gratitude when he was focussing on a rather gaudy woodpecker and I came from nowhere to shake old beaky up a bit! It's hardly my fault he wasn't quick enough to snap it flapping into the woods. As I progressed to catching my own mice, I often presented him with one in an effort to be helpful. I know they sometimes didn't have heads, but a bit of artistic flair could have turned them into iconic images.

I was also developing into something of a hide-and-seek champion. As fast as they discovered my hidey-holes, I made it my business to find new ones. The drawer under the bed was a good one because for a long time they thought it was Count Lucio and not little old me. It was the Earth Mother who became suspicious – mainly because Lucio was in full view helping himself to Bun-Bun's special diet food – and rushed back into the bedroom to grope in the drawer to see if there were any feet on the back legs.

'There aren't any feet!' she shouted, scaring the wits out of Poor Roger who was half asleep on the sofa and assumed some virulent toe-nibbling virus must have struck; Miss Elizabeth reported he was greatly relieved to find his feet were still snugly attached to his legs under Benjamin's comatose body.

One night I managed to hide in the shadowy corner by the patio door and sneak into the garden when Poor Roger stumbled out into the night to feed the old feral tarts, Delilah and Spitfire. This was quite a triumph as the humans were obsessed with getting me in before darkness fell and I'd been banged up hours previously. I had a wonderful time out there, venturing into the woods as soon as the badger tunnel was opened and scampering around with Evie; the smells were so exciting that I kept squeaking until Evie smacked me round the head for sabotaging her hunting endeavours.

Just before midnight we were back in the garden tossing a mouse around and generally having a good time when that stupid fox came trotting past and activated the security light. We could see the Earth Mother and Poor Roger slumped on the sofa and unfortunately they could see us.

'I thought that was Stumpy for a moment!' trilled the Earth Mother, parting the cobwebs to peer through the patio door. 'Obviously it isn't because he's been in for hours.'

'It must be Evie,' mused Poor Roger, as Evie rushed up to me and grabbed the mouse.

It took them a while, but eventually even they realised that they were looking at two cats and whisked me back indoors.

The strange thing was that although I was obviously absolutely fine, they couldn't resist torturing themselves about what terrible things *could* have happened to me. By the time they reached the bit about me being taken hostage by homicidal badgers, I decided to vote with my paws – both of them.

CHAPTER ELEVEN

A Winter's Tail

Miss Elizabeth was the only resident who had always realised that life at Tresta Towers would still be unpredictable and full of cats and cat people when the Earth Mother retired. Poor Roger, having already suffered many disappointments on the domestic front, still clung to the belief that there might be the odd half hour when the Earth Mother wouldn't be gabbling and cackling into the phone or hosting bizarre tea parties, where the latest flea and worm treatments competed for top billing with used cat litter disposal problems and the administration of gob-stopper sized cat tablets.

At one point he had naively voiced the hope that the odd weekend away might feature on the agenda. This unfounded optimism illustrates once again how humans fail to learn from experience. Show me the cat that voluntarily clambers into a cat carrier and pleads to be taken to the vet again after just one brief visit! Oops – I forgot about St Petersburg Cloud Princess, but Persians aren't really cats; they're more like some sort of inbred gremlin thing from an undiscovered planet.

As winter made its presence felt, a particularly scary feature of life here was the worry about Tammy-Wammy-Woo-Woo. This concern dated from the evening that Poor Roger and the Earth Mother visited one of their cronies and met Tammy-Wammy for the first time. They lurched back around midnight, merry as kittens on catnip, and proceeded to regale us with more information than a roomful of sleepy cats could possibly have wanted about a dog.

'I loved the way she tossed those dreadlocks about!' trilled the Earth Mother, 'and kept putting her head on one side!'

None of us remembered their friend Abi having dreadlocks, or putting her head on one side any more than the next person. The next utterance was downright alarming.

'I could hardly see you when she got on your lap. And when she knocked your glasses on the floor – that was really funny!' sniggered Poor Roger.

The Earth Mother obviously didn't find this quite so rib-ticklingly amusing, but Tammy-Wammy's charms were more than enough to overcome this minor blip.

'If someone had told me I'd fall in love with a labradoodle, I'd have thought they'd lost their marbles,' she said in her kindly way, 'but Tammy-Wammy is wonderful!'

A photograph of this canine icon duly appeared. Benjamin Wobble immediately broke ranks by observing that she looked as if she'd be a lot more fun than Miss Elizabeth, which earned him a smack in the chops, while Evie absent-mindedly shredded a catnip toy and Bella emerged from her igloo to sneeze over the Earth Mother's handbag.

'Of course, now we're around much more we could think about having a dog,' mused the Earth Mother tactlessly.

Whizzy, who was snoozing on her lap, shot off, only to spend the next ten minutes extricating a strip of human skin from her manicured paw.

'I don't think it would be fair to the dog,' responded Poor Roger. 'You imagine the poor creature arriving here to be confronted by this lot! It would be like that dreadful interview when I went for that job in Chertsey, but even they didn't spit at me or try to claw my eyes out!'

'It would be nice to have an animal that actually wanted to be with you all the time and loved you more than anything else in the world,' droned the Earth Mother, ignoring Poor Roger's remembered pain. 'I often think the cats don't really care whether we're here or not – and they look at me sometimes as if they think I'm stupid!'

I was amazed that she'd noticed that. Perhaps we should have made more effort to appear fascinated when she was wittering on about Bun-Bun's latest thyroid reading or the difficulty she was experiencing with getting rid of the cat wee smell on the back seat of the car. I immediately focussed on her melon-like face with every ounce of concentration I could muster, only to be snapped at for staring at her in an intimidating manner.

In the end, help came from an unlikely source when Bonnie Bun-Bun's latest crop of blood test results indicated there was wear and tear on the kidneys and the vet said she needed to have as little stress in her life as possible. Leaving aside the fact that the old coat-hanger was twenty-one years old, I would hazard a guess that the only things with less stress in their lives than Bun-Bun were probably blind invertebrates groping around at the bottom of the sea.

Anyway, although the Earth Mother and Poor Roger remained besotted with Tammy-Wammy, we heard no more about a clone of this canine goddess disrupting our really quite pleasant lives. Meanwhile, Bun-Bun's kidneys received star treatment with special diet food being purchased at great expense. Bun-Bun could take or leave this pallid mush, but Benjamin was desperate to cram as much down as he could possibly manage before the Earth Mother spotted him and subjected him to the terrors of the flapping tea towel and a bracing speech.

Another reason for Bun-Bun being cosseted was her recent and sudden bereavement. Poor Great Uncle Tigger had shuffled off to the Great Dirt Tray in the sky and the Earth Mother was convinced that Bun-Bun would miss him desperately. There were no indications that she did, but Bun-Bun graciously allowed herself to be pampered and fussed over, probably feeling she was doing the Earth Mother a favour. Miss Isabelle said she couldn't remember Tigger at all, but a couple of days had passed when I mentioned him so that was hardly surprising.

Christmas had just slipped past with yummy platefuls of turkey and – even better – tasty chunks of gammon. I really loved that gammon, but the Earth Mother was no fun at all and wouldn't let me have more than a taste because, apparently, there was too much salt in it and it would be bad for me. Why it was perfectly acceptable for her to cram it down in portions that would have defeated a hungry lion was never made clear.

One morning I looked out of the patio door and saw that the garden had disappeared. No – I don't mean the pointy-nosed badgers had finally excavated it out of existence; it was just completely white.

'How lovely!' trilled the Earth Mother when she emerged. 'It must have been snowing all night. Look, Stumpy Malone – real snow!'

Once I knew that the world hadn't ended, I couldn't wait to get out there and was throwing it around in no time. It wasn't long, however, before I realised that the ends of my back legs were very cold indeed and I had to come back indoors. I'd never worried about my missing paws before, but I certainly could have done with them in the snow. The Earth Mother toyed with the idea of socks, but mercifully decided that she wouldn't be able to attach them firmly enough, so my excursions into this new and exciting world had to be limited to half hour bursts.

Irritatingly, I could see Evie prancing around outside, diving into drifts of snow and flinging herself up trees while I was banged up inside with all the old dribblers and Count Lucio, who made much of his Italian heritage; this apparently meant he had to stay in bed all day when the temperature dropped below 30 degrees centigrade, which meant he generally ventured out for about five days a year.

The cold spell had the Earth Mother reaching for her trusty Damart catalogue and placing an order for essential items. For a while we thought this could signify the end of the dinosaur sweatshirt era, only to have our hopes dashed when the parcel arrived. Excitement reached unprecedented levels as the Earth Mother extracted a strange and extremely large single slipper and what looked like an enormous heap of candyfloss once it was released from its plastic bag.

All was revealed that very evening when Miss Isabelle rushed into the kitchen to inform us that a large pink polar bear had fallen over in the lounge and was swearing in a manner reminiscent of the Earth Mother.

The voluminous pink dressing gown was bad enough, but whatever had possessed the woman who could trip over a feather to purchase a foot muff, I shall never know. Inevitably, it turned out to be Whizzy's fault for appearing at the patio door and forcing the Earth Mother to plunge across the room, quite forgetting both feet were trapped in the cosy foot muff.

Miss Elizabeth had always said that the weeks after Christmas were a very dangerous time and I was beginning to realise what a sharp little brain lurks under that rather poor quality fur.

Poor Roger had received some money for Christmas and decided to splash out on a close-up lens with which to record the smaller and less showy forms of wildlife rash enough to visit our garden. Immediate testing of the new acquisition was obviously essential and our hero soon pronounced himself extremely satisfied with the results. So far, so good, but why he felt it would be a good idea to show the Earth Mother the fruits of his labours on a large and brightly lit computer screen remains a mystery. I'm not saying the Earth Mother's face was scary in close-up, but nobody looks their best when snoring on the sofa with their mouth open.

A high spot of the gloomy winter months was the gathering of the neighbours for what the Earth Mother insists on calling a soiree, but which actually takes place in the middle of the day – the theory being that we will be merrily romping round the garden while they're all cackling away indoors. Well, Evie and I ventured out first thing, but hadn't got as far as the badgers' supper station before the heavens opened and chucked down another load of snow on our little black heads.

Seeing what had happened to us, the others clamped down on the sofas and stared at the Earth Mother in disbelief when she suggested popping out for some fresh air. Miss Elizabeth coughed dramatically and Benjamin embarked on a panicky bonking routine with his bed, while Count Lucio maintained a dignified silence in the depths of the wardrobe.

By the time the neighbours arrived, the battle for sofa space had assumed epic proportions. Miss Elizabeth jumped down, but managed to swipe several smoked salmon nibbles off a tray in the course of her descent; Bun-Bun stepped over the guacamole dip, emerging with glutinous green lumps dropping from her sagging undercarriage, and Benjamin buried his fuzzy little face in the sausages, scattering them liberally and greasily across various pastel-clad laps.

As darkness loomed, St Petersburg Cloud Princess emerged from her igloo on the dining table to gaze blearily at the assembled company. The Earth Mother was across the room in a tottering run, pausing only to equip herself with kitchen roll and air freshener, as the ancient Persian legged it into the bedroom to grunt and piddle in the darkest corner.

Some of the neighbours were getting a bit restless by this stage, but the Earth Mother had them cornered with a cheese and onion quiche and some garlic bread that could have felled an ox. I felt that the time had come to perform my party piece and crossed the lounge by walking just on my front paws. This had always been a show-stopper and on this occasion generated a superior level of discussion, encompassing the Paralympics and some poor man who had recently had a successful hand transplant. This made me a bit nervous in case the Earth Mother suddenly thought about getting me some old cat's cast offs. It might have worked, but it would have been just my luck for the donor to be an enormous Norwegian Forest cat, or some shaggy old ginger tom... With my thin little black legs I'd look like a feline version of Mickey Mouse.

Our guests' reasons for extricating themselves took on an increasingly fanciful quality as time went on; one remembered he had to collect a parcel of frozen peas from the sorting office, another that she'd come without some vital medication and a third that a nameless distant relative needed picking up at the airport. Most compelling of all was the possibility of more snow – a real hazard when you live three doors down the road. In the end, the Earth Mother had to give in and unlock the door, comforted by the knowledge that she had helped them to realise how straightforward their own cat-free lives were. They were all besotted with me, naturally, and kept saying what a brave little soldier I was and how lucky I was to have such a caring home. Caring? What did they know! If she'd really cared, the Earth Mother wouldn't have let me steal that Scotch egg. The bloody thing settled like ballast in my stomach and I fell into a burp-filled coma, missing *Winterwatch* with all those yummy birds and mice.

Speaking of which reminds me of another highlight in the January calendar – the RSPB bird count. Miss Elizabeth had warned me about this, but nothing could have prepared me for the tensions and stresses which accompanied this supposedly innocuous project. The Earth Mother and Poor Roger would settle down, notebooks to hand, peering optimistically at the bird feeders. All was sweetness and light until the first bird arrived.

'Right – that's obviously a blue tit and I'm counting it!' sang out the Earth Mother.

'Blue Tit? That's a Great Tit if ever I saw one!' countered Poor Roger, dropping his notebook in an excess of emotion.

And so it went on, until Evie decided to take things into her own paws and jumped at the bird feeders in a spectacular – and doomed – attempt to bring in Mr Mystery Tit for closer inspection.

The tension was sustained until the completed survey was finally winging its way to the unsuspecting RSPB, where one can only begin to imagine the excitement caused by an osprey landing in the suburbs of Woking.

Soon after this challenging experience, I nipped into the cupboard which passes for a study to steal some of Evie's biscuits, only to find the Earth Mother wiping her eyes and making strange, Persian-like snuffling noises. I was about to make my apologies and scamper away when she snatched me up.

'Wonderful news, Stumpy! Your brother's been found alive and well!'

I was obviously pleased to know that all was well with old Woody, but as I hadn't realised he was missing in the first place my reaction may have been a trifle muted. Apparently poor old Woody had been missing since September and the Earth Mother hadn't told me because she didn't want me to be upset. He'd been found a couple of streets away from his new home, which confirmed what I'd always suspected: he had the paws, but I had the brains!

CHAPTER TWELVE

Furry Friends

As we shuffled into another spring, the Earth Mother decided to have an eczema outbreak – something she tended to do when there was nothing on the telly. This was pretty boring, apart from moments of hysteria caused by the liberal use of oily preparations in the shower. This particular comedy routine featured a great deal of swearing and crashing about and after a prolonged interval the bathroom door would be flung open, with the Earth Mother issuing forth in clouds of steam.

'I thought you'd be there, Stumpy Malone!' she'd splutter, extending a hand like a cow's udder, 'don't get upset, darling, Mummy's just a bit bruised. You're such a sweet boy to worry.'

Well, I hadn't actually been all that worried. I was just waiting to get into the bathroom so I could unravel the toilet roll like those plump and rather stupid looking puppies in the advert.

An extremely worrying development around this time was the ill-advised passion that minxy little Evie conceived for the dog fox. This was no ordinary fox, but a veritable David Beckham among foxes, who might well have won the Supreme Championship at Crufts if he'd taken the trouble to think about the subsequent marketing opportunities. Whether or not there was a foxy equivalent of Posh Spice lurking in the undergrowth, pouting and posturing, we never established. Anyway, the Earth Mother and Poor Roger were obsessed with us being eaten by this vulpine eye candy, but – being the mass of contradictions that humans seem to be – couldn't wait to ply him with goodies as soon as he daubed his snotty nose on the patio door.

Evie could often be seen cosying up to her hero under the pine tree which sent everybody into emotional overdrive; the humans because Freddie Fox couldn't be trusted, Delilah and Spitfire because these feral matriarchs liked nothing better than to mop up the supper slapped down for Freddie and the bulky old badgers, and Count Lucio, who had conceived a violent hatred of foxes in general and of Freddie in particular.

All of this was quite confusing for poor old foxy-chops as he never quite worked out whether it was little black Evie or big black Lucio emerging from the shadows and sustained many a bell-ringing slap from the latter as a result. After such an encounter, our feline hero would gallop back indoors, do several circuits of the bungalow at head height and settle on the work top to pick any residual foxy debris from his panther-sized paws.

There was never any doubt that the pointy-faced badgers were at the top of the heap and as soon as they arrived Freddie would skulk behind the pine tree, waiting for Moonbeam and Brillo to rake over the goodies. They would do this with irritating slowness, holding up a custard cream or a lump of cake in their great curved claws and sniffing it before condescending to cram it into their cavernous mouths. This used to drive the Earth Mother mad.

'Look at that bloody badger!' she would mutter, her fat face pressed against the window, 'how dare he look at my muffins like that? Surely anything would be yummier than worms!'

Benjamin Wobble could always be relied upon to provide light relief in moments of tension, although there were those that felt it was inappropriate to expose his undercarriage quite so blatantly when a visiting male crony was discussing a sensitive and particularly personal operation. Another speciality was sliding from the sofa into open handbags – an attention-seeking ploy which he'd perfected over the years. Miss Elizabeth said she had treasured hopes that he might end up being carried off to far-flung regions, but we were never that lucky. At the sight of those flailing ginger paws, the visitor and the Earth Mother would rush to extricate poor Benjy, often sustaining concussion in the process as their heads collided.

Of the three feral girls, black Spitfire was easily the wildest. She'd lived here for thirteen years, consumed a mountain of food and still looked at the Earth Mother and Poor Roger as if they'd crawled out of a particularly smelly swamp. Delilah, the empty-headed tortoiseshell, allowed herself to be stroked at feeding time, but only if Spitfire wasn't looking. Piebald Pansy – when she took time out from being Tonypandy, the "boy" cat from down the road – thought nothing of pushing past the Earth Mother's chunky legs to give our dishes the once-over in the kitchen, so it was very much left to Spitfire to keep faith with the feral creed, which could be summarised as, "Take what you can get and spit in their faces".

Everybody was happy to indulge Spitfire in this slavish adherence to her religious beliefs, but a run-in with a stray tom cat turned poor old Spitfire from a fur-clad missile into a hobbling wreck. Poor Roger was beside himself.

'Spitfire trusts me,' he sighed, 'and when she most needs my help, I don't know what to do. That tom cat's got a lot to answer for. Poor Spitsy's hiding away in her cabin, looking at me. I can see the pain in her eyes.'

The Earth Mother adopted a brisker approach. 'What you can see in her eyes is a desire to kill you,' she remarked helpfully. 'I'll get some antibiotics from the vet and we'll grind them up in her food. Unless you'd like to pop them down her throat, of course!'

Several days later, after much purposeful mashing of diamond-hard pink tablets, the Earth Mother announced that Spitfire seemed much more like her old self – that is to say, pretty bloody awful. The enforced rest had done nothing to improve her temper and she erupted from her bed of pain to wage a war of attrition on every male cat she could get her paws on. This was a particularly trying time for Benjamin Wobble as Spitfire entirely failed to register the presence of this testosterone-fuelled humbug, treading all over him to savage myself and dear Lucio, leaving Benjy to salvage what he could of his macho pride.

As for the stray tom, we soon found that a neighbour had succumbed to his manly charms and in no time at all this huge black bully boy was strolling around looking considerably sleeker and quite dashing if you liked that sort of thing; perhaps I was alone in wondering if the pink glittery collar was entirely appropriate, but I certainly wasn't going to be the one to mention it.

I have previously mentioned the worrying time we went through when it seemed possible that a clone of

Tammy-Wammy-Woo-Woo, the dreadlocked labradoodle, might be coming to live with us. Once we realised this was never going to happen, we began to feel quite warmly towards the poor creature and decided to make allowances for her being a dog. It was a particularly wet and windy Sunday afternoon when our friend Abi phoned with the news that Tammy was seriously ill. Poor old Tammy had been whipped into hospital, languishing in her kennel with a horrible drip thing in her hairy arm.

The vet kept saying that Tammy wouldn't get better unless she ate something, but as various tempting morsels of chicken were wafted under her dry nose, Tammy looked about as disgusted as a pig being forced to contemplate a jar of apple sauce. This depressing state of affairs had continued for several days when an unlikely hero arrived on the scene.

Abi had spent a knee crunching hour trying to persuade Tammy that it would be a really good idea to eat something. She'd done the "one for Mummy, one for Tammy" routine without arousing so much as a flicker of mild curiosity and was preparing to leave when a scrabbling noise from the opposite kennel attracted her interest. Siegfried, the miniature dachshund, had just regained consciousness after a minor operation and had smelt the freshly cooked chicken. Within seconds, this animated sausage was squeaking and scrabbling at the bars, while Tammy opened one bloodshot eye and raised her head off her paws.

With heart-stopping slowness, she reached out and took a fragment of chicken from Abi's hand and, as Siegfried's yelps reached a crescendo, she took another piece. Abi burst into tears and the vet discovered he'd got something in his eye that made it water. Tammy-Wammy-Woo-Woo had decided to make a fight of it.

At the same time as all this was going on, for some reason best known to themselves, the Earth Mother and Poor Roger decided to embark on a "Big Adventure". No – not a trip to the Galapagos, although the Earth Mother was particularly fascinated by the marine iguanas' salt-snorting abilities – but a visit to the local cinema to see *Les Miserables*. Predictably, they arrived home with puffy, tearstained faces which almost put me off my supper. The Earth Mother lurched through the door and grabbed the nearest bottle of El Plonko, downing a glass before Poor Roger had turned off the burglar alarm.

'What an emotional roller-coaster that was!' she snuffled noisily, 'there were three women in floods of tears in the ladies!'

'Still, I really enjoyed it,' sniffed Poor Roger, 'we must go and see the stage show some time.'

Miss Elizabeth curled her lip and commented caustically that she was pleased they'd enjoyed themselves so much and, after an evening of snuffling and sniffing while they punished themselves further by listening to the music from the show, even I was beginning to think that a bit of energetic salt-snorting would have been preferable.

By now, with Tammy-Wammy well on the way to recovery and Spitfire fully restored to her usual level of unpleasantness, the Earth Mother and Poor Roger were running short of things to worry about and we were concerned that their attention could turn to routine maintenance – as in flea treatments and ear cleaning. Fortunately, St Petersburg Cloud Princess managed to fill in quite a few idle moments by developing some deeply unattractive lumps of fur on her undercarriage, giving rise to "Operation Candyfloss".

Poor Roger would gather up the old mop and the Earth Mother would approach with the shaver.

'I'm going in!' she would say in a shrill, tense voice. 'For God's sake, you've got your finger right over the lump – and hold her leg! Oh – it's not her leg! It must be that brandy snap biscuit I left on the table.'

Occasionally, the Earth Mother would actually be holding the shaver thing the right way up, but this didn't often happen. Being the animated creature she was, our fuzzy little princess tended to nod off in Poor Roger's arms while the Earth Mother was sorting herself out, waking up in time to peer wonderingly at the pile of rather grubby-looking fur on the dining room table at the end of the grooming session.

On one occasion when old fuzzy-chops was having a major makeover at the vet's, the Earth Mother came dangerously close to stuffing the pile of fur into the cat carrier instead of our diminutive heroine, but the absence of snuffling gave the game away.

Miss Elizabeth's flapping heart valve had long been cause for concern, necessitating regular blood tests to establish whether the old bag should start having medication, and the Earth Mother suddenly realised with a guilty flush that the time had come to pop old Lizzie down the road and give the vet a treat.

Unless it was a real crisis, the Earth Mother used to enjoy these outings; inevitably she would meet some of her cronies and more often than not some poor innocent creature who had been tricked into taking on some appalling rescue cat during her homing officer days.

Lizzie confirmed that this had indeed been the case on this latest trip, with the additional bonus of an embarrassing interlude. Apparently, a man had staggered into the waiting room, wrestling with a pop-eyed cat who was making a good job of redesigning his face. He was followed by a desperate-looking woman, who gasped out their appointment time to the receptionist and proceeded to shout at "Stanley" to pull himself together. The Earth Mother immediately launched into a lecture about the dangers of carrying a cat in their arms and the need for a cat carrier, while Elizabeth settled herself down to enjoy the fun.

'You really must get a secure cat carrier,' chirped the Earth Mother. 'Even if Stanley is very confident at home, he's bound to be terrified being carried past all those cars on the way in. And look – there's a dog over there! Stanley's probably never seen one before!'

The woman regarded the Earth Mother in amazement before gathering her wits sufficiently to point out that "Stanley" was in fact her husband and that the cat was called "Muldoon". Ignoring this detail, the Earth Mother had by now swept across to the receptionist and advised her in ringing tones that this hapless couple should be lent a cat carrier forthwith, if not sooner.

The dog – an overweight spaniel with bloodshot eyes – appeared not to have noticed Muldoon's arrival, and it was unfortunate that Muldoon had noticed him as he was now demonstrating a strong desire to rip the dog to bits. By now Stanley's arms were shredded and Muldoon had succeeded in ripping the watch from his bleeding wrist, smashing it on the floor in a cavalier gesture. Further entertainment was provided by the sight of Muldoon's owners threading him into a front-loading carrier of somewhat cramped proportions, giving the Earth Mother yet another excuse for berating them.

'Back him in! Then he won't be able to brace himself!' she yelled encouragingly.

After all this, Miss Elizabeth's blood test was a bit of an anticlimax, but as she saw the Earth Mother wielding two credit cards to pay the bill, our plucky heroine felt at that least she'd had her money's worth.

I was just relaxing after this heartwarming episode when the Earth Mother started tickling me behind the ear.

'Stumpy's got one!' she shrieked, 'and it's huge!'

Benjamin Wobble threw me an admiring look before slumping back into his miniature four-poster and Miss Isabelle yawned in slow motion. I didn't know whether to be alarmed or flattered, but it soon became obvious that alarm would be by far the more appropriate emotion as the Earth Mother advanced with an instrument of torture which should have been banned centuries ago under some convention or the other.

Seconds later, she was holding a bloated lump in the air. No – not Benjamin Wobble, but a thing like a rubbery grape, which had been sucking my life blood according to the Earth Mother. So that was the end of Mr Tick and pretty well the end of me. It wasn't the tick that was the problem really; it was all the kissing and hugging that followed, with the Earth Mother telling me what a brave little kitten-cat I'd been.

Actually, people are always telling me I'm a brave cat because I'm missing a couple of paws, but after two years without them I wouldn't know what to do with hind paws if they arrived in the post. Everybody here is missing something or has too much of something, including the Earth Mother and Poor Roger: she's always saying the El Plonko stocks are running low and he's always ordering up a load of puppy pads just as St Petersburg Cloud Princess has decided that using them compromises her religious or political beliefs – or that she just likes using the floor.

Even the cats who appear normal are pretty challenged. Count Lucio, the Italian stallion, suffers from "dinosaurs' disease" – having a large body with a pea-sized brain – and Evie has recently decided she can't eat her food without being stroked by the Earth Mother or Poor Roger.

Of the more obviously afflicted, Bonnie Bun-Bun is a martyr to dementia, over-active thyroid and kidney problems, while Whizzy still can't remember where she left her missing leg; Miss Elizabeth's heart condition means she gets away with just about anything and Miss Isabelle has never been anything other than woefully inadequate. Benjamin Wobble dribbles away in his own fuzzy little world and the Persian is a walking disaster. The three wild girls are probably pretty normal, but most ferals don't have their own sleeping bags as far as I'm aware.

So when we get down to it, I think that being perfect would be a major handicap here at Tresta Towers. Between you and me, I'm quite pleased I ended up here, but this is just the start as far as I'm concerned. I keep imagining my adoring fans weeping with happiness as I accept yet another Olympic gold medal and parade before them with a Union Jack billowing behind my impossibly toned, Lycra-clad body. I would stop frequently to make that familiar and iconic "S" sign with my long black tail, probably with the Managing Director of Webbox trailing along behind and begging me to accept a complimentary box of his yummy cat treats. Where is Rio anyway?